VERSE
WORTH REMEMBERING

SELECTED BY

STANLEY MAXWELL, M.A., LL.B.

LATE SECRETARY OF THE COLLEGE OF PRECEPTORS
FORMER HEADMASTER, MANOR HOUSE SCHOOL, CLAPHAM

WITH A FOREWORD BY

FRANK ROSCOE, M.A.

DEAN OF THE COLLEGE OF PRECEPTORS
PAST SECRETARY, ROYAL SOCIETY OF TEACHERS

MACMILLAN AND CO., LIMITED
ST. MARTIN'S STREET, LONDON

1955

First Edition 1940
Reprinted 1941, 1942, 1943, 1944, 1946, 1947, 1950, 1952, 1955.

PRINTED IN GREAT BRITAIN

Foreword

In a well-known essay Francis Bacon says that " Studies serve for delight, for ornament, and for ability." The order is important, since it tells us that in obtaining knowledge we should find pleasure and acquire ease and grace of mind, instead of thinking only of gaining the kind of skill which will bring money. It is possible to be rich in money while being poor in things which cannot be bought but are essential to real happiness in life.

Among these indispensable things is the power to enjoy poetry, and in this collection Mr. Stanley Maxwell has brought together examples of poetry which represent every accepted form of the art. Wisely he has avoided any attempt to build up a text-book, and has omitted the all too familiar order of dates and the explanatory notes which serve only to hamper enjoyment and to minister to the requirements of examinations. The book used with intelligence and enthusiasm in the classroom, will serve the purpose of any sensible examination. It will give delight and foster a discriminating taste instead of provoking the resolve to avoid all poetry when schooldays are ended.

Some such resolve has been the lamentable result of our conventional method of introducing children to poetry. Instead of opening their eyes to its beauties we have placed them in blinkers contrived by linguistic pedants. Without such blinkers and with the minimum of formal teaching children will respond to the rhythm and melody of well-chosen verse such as this volume contains.

F. R.

Acknowledgments

PERMISSION for the use of copyright poems in this Anthology has kindly been given by the following :—Mr. Hilaire Belloc and Messrs. Gerald Duckworth & Co., Ltd. ; the representatives of Lewis Carroll ; Messrs. Chatto & Windus, for " The Celestial Surgeon," by R. L. Stevenson ; the Clarendon Press, Oxford, for " First Spring Morning," from *The Shorter Poems of Robert Bridges* ; Mr. Walter de la Mare ; Messrs. J. M. Dent & Sons, Ltd., for " The Donkey," by G. K. Chesterton ; Lady Conan Doyle and Messrs. John Murray, for " The Song of the Bow," from *Songs of Action*, by Sir A. Conan Doyle ; the Executors of the late Mrs. Hardy, for " The Oxen," from *Collected Poems of Thomas Hardy* ; the Executors of W. E. Henley ; Mr. Ralph Hodgson ; the late Mrs. Kipling, for " If—", from *Rewards and Fairies*, " A Smuggler's Song," from *Puck of Pook's Hill*, and " The Camel's Hump," from *Just So Stories*, by Rudyard Kipling ; Mr. John Masefield, for " Sea Fever," from *Collected Poems of John Masefield* (Wm. Heinemann, Ltd.) ; the Executors of the late Sir Henry Newbolt, for " Vitaï Lampada," " Drake's Drum " and " Admirals All," from his *Poems New and Old* (John Murray) ; Mr. Alfred Noyes and Messrs. Wm. Blackwood & Sons, Ltd., for " A Song of England " and " At Kew," from *Collected Poems of Alfred Noyes* ; Mr. Lloyd Osbourne, for the poems from *A Child's Garden of Verses*, by R. L. Stevenson ; the Oxford University Press and the author's Executors, for " A Ballade to Queen Elizabeth," by Austin Dobson ; Lady Spring Rice and Messrs. Longmans Green & Co., Ltd., for " I Vow to Thee, my Country," from *Poems*, by the late Sir Cecil Spring Rice ; Sir John Squire ; and the representatives of Lord Tennyson.

Contents

v

vi   Contents

Contents

viii Contents

PART I

A*

My Shadow

ROBERT LOUIS STEVENSON

I HAVE a little shadow that goes in and out with me,
And what can be the use of him is more than I can see.
He is very very like me from the heels up to the head:
And I see him jump before me when I jump into my
    bed.

The funniest thing about him is the way he likes to grow—
Not at all like proper children, which is always very slow;
For he sometimes shoots up taller, like an indiarubber
    ball,
And he sometimes gets so little that there's none of him at
    all.

He hasn't got a notion of how children ought to play,
And can only make a fool of me in every sort of way.
He stays so close beside me, he's a coward you can see;
I'd think it shame to stick to nursie as that shadow sticks
    to me!

One morning, very early, before the sun was up,
I rose and found the shining dew on every buttercup:
But my lazy little shadow, like an arrant sleepy-head,
Had stayed at home behind me and was fast asleep in
    bed.

3

The Lamplighter

ROBERT LOUIS STEVENSON

My tea is nearly ready, and the sun has left the sky;
It's time to take the window to see Leerie going by;
For every night at tea-time, and before you take your
    seat,
With lantern and with ladder he comes posting up the
    street.

Now Tom would be a driver, and Maria go to sea,
And my papa's a banker, and as rich as he can be;
But I, when I am stronger, and can choose what I'm to
    do,
O Leerie, I'll go round at night and light the lamps with
    you!

For we are very lucky, with a lamp before the door,
And Leerie stops to light it as he lights so many more;
And O! before you hurry by with ladder and with light,
O Leerie, see a little child and nod to him to-night!

Escape at Bedtime

ROBERT LOUIS STEVENSON

The lights from the parlour and kitchen shone out
    Through the blinds and the windows and bars;
And high overhead and all moving about,
    There were thousands of millions of stars.
There ne'er were such thousands of leaves on a tree,
    Nor of people in church or the Park,
As the crowds of the stars that looked down upon me,
    And that glittered and winked in the dark.

The Dog, and the Plough, and the Hunter, and all,
   And the star of the sailor, and Mars,
These shone in the sky, and the pail by the wall
   Would be half full of water and stars.
They saw me at last, and they chased me with cries,
   And they soon had me packed into bed;
But the glory kept shining and bright in my eyes,
   And the stars going round in my head.

Shadow March

ROBERT LOUIS STEVENSON

ALL round the house is the jet-black night;
   It stares through the window-pane;
It crawls in the corners, hiding from the light,
   And it moves with the moving flame.

Now my little heart goes a-beating like a drum,
   With the breath of the Bogie in my hair;
And all round the candle the crooked shadows come
   And go marching along up the stair.

The shadow of the balusters, the shadow of the lamp,
   The shadow of the child that goes to bed—
All the wicked shadows coming, tramp, tramp, tramp,
   With the black night overhead.

Round the Year

COVENTRY PATMORE

THE crocus, while the days are dark,
   Unfolds its saffron sheen;
At April's touch, the crudest bark
   Discovers gems of green.

Then sleep the seasons, full of might,
    While slowly swells the pod
And rounds the peach, and in the night
    The mushroom bursts the sod.

The winter comes: the frozen rut
    Is bound with silver bars;
The snow-drift heaps against the hut;
    And night is pierced with stars.

Lady Moon

LORD HOUGHTON

LADY Moon, Lady Moon, where are you roving?
    " Over the sea."
Lady Moon, Lady Moon, whom are you loving?
    " All that love me."

Are you not tired with rolling, and never
    Resting to sleep?
Why look so pale and so sad, as for ever
    Wishing to weep?

" Ask me not this, little child, if you love me;
    You are too bold.
I must obey my dear Father above me,
    And do as I'm told."

Lady Moon, Lady Moon, where are you roving?
    " Over the sea."
Lady Moon, Lady Moon, whom are you loving?
    " All that love me."

Queen Mab

THOMAS HOOD

A LITTLE fairy comes at night,
  Her eyes are blue, her hair is brown,
With silver spots upon her wings,
  And from the moon she flutters down.

She has a little silver wand,
  And when a good child goes to bed
She waves her hand from right to left,
  And makes a circle round its head.

And then it dreams of pleasant things,
  Of fountains filled with fairy fish,
And trees that bear delicious fruit,
  And bow their branches at a wish:

Of arbours filled with dainty scents
  From lovely flowers that never fade;
Bright flies that glitter in the sun,
  And glow-worms shining in the shade;

And talking birds with gifted tongues
  For singing songs and telling tales,
And pretty dwarfs to show the way
  Through fairy hills and fairy dales.

But when a bad child goes to bed,
  From left to right she weaves her rings,
And then it dreams all through the night
  Of only ugly horrid things!

The Fairies

WILLIAM ALLINGHAM

Up the airy mountain,
  Down the rushy glen,
We daren't go a-hunting
  For fear of little men;
Wee folk, good folk,
  Trooping all together;
Green jacket, red cap,
  And white owl's feather!

Down along the rocky shore
  Some make their home,
They live on crispy pancakes
  Of yellow tide-foam;
Some in the reeds
  Of the black mountain lake,
With frogs for the watch-dogs,
  All night awake.

High on the hill-top
  The old King sits;
He is now so old and gray,
  He's nigh lost his wits.
With a bridge of white mist
  Columbkill he crosses
On his stately journeys
  From Slieveleague to Rosses;
Or going up with music
  On cold, starry nights,
To sup with the Queen
  Of the gay Northern Lights.

They stole little Bridget
  For seven years long;
When she came down again
  Her friends were all gone.
They took her lightly back,
  Between the night and morrow,
They thought that she was fast asleep,
  But she was dead with sorrow.
They have kept her ever since
  Deep within the lake,
On a bed of flag leaves,
  Watching till she wake.

By the craggy hill-side,
  Through the mosses bare,
They have planted thorn-trees
  For pleasure here and there.
Is any man so daring
  As dig them up in spite,
He shall find their sharpest thorns
  In his bed at night.

Up the airy mountain,
  Down the rushy glen,
We daren't go a-hunting
  For fear of little men;
Wee folk, good folk,
  Trooping all together;
Green jacket, red cap,
  And white owl's feather!

M.V.

First Spring Morning

ROBERT BRIDGES

Look! Look! the spring is come:
 O feel the gentle air,
That wanders thro' the boughs to burst
 The thick buds everywhere!
 The birds are glad to see
 The high unclouded sun:
Winter is fled away, they sing,
 The gay time is begun.

 Adown the meadows green
 Let us go dance and play,
And look for violets in the lane,
 And ramble far away
 To gather primroses,
 That in the woodland grow,
And hunt for oxlips, or if yet
 The blades of bluebells show:

 There the old woodman gruff
 Hath half the coppice cut,
And weaves the hurdles all day long
 Beside his willow hut.
 We'll steal on him, and then
 Startle him, all with glee
Singing our song of winter fled
 And summer soon to be.

The Village Blacksmith

H. W. LONGFELLOW

UNDER a spreading chestnut-tree
  The village smithy stands;
The smith, a mighty man is he,
  With large and sinewy hands;
And the muscles of his brawny arms
  Are strong as iron bands.

His hair is crisp, and black, and long,
  His face is like the tan;
His brow is wet with honest sweat,
  He earns whate'er he can,
And looks the whole world in the face,
  For he owes not any man.

Week in, week out, from morn till night,
  You can hear his bellows blow;
You can hear him swing his heavy sledge,
  With measured beat and slow,
Like a sexton ringing the village bell,
  When the evening sun is low.

And children coming home from school
  Look in at the open door;
They love to see the flaming forge,
  And hear the bellows roar,
And catch the burning sparks that fly
  Like chaff from a threshing-floor.

He goes on Sunday to the church,
  And sits among his boys;

He hears the parson pray and preach,
  He hears his daughter's voice
Singing in the village choir,
  And it makes his heart rejoice.

It sounds to him like her mother's voice,
  Singing in Paradise!
He needs must think of her once more,
  How in the grave she lies;
And with his hard, rough hand he wipes
  A tear out of his eyes.

Toiling—rejoicing—sorrowing,
  Onward through life he goes;
Each morning sees some task begin,
  Each evening sees it close;
Something attempted, something done,
  Has earned a night's repose.

Thanks, thanks, to thee, my worthy friend,
  For the lesson thou hast taught!
Thus at the flaming forge of life
  Our fortunes must be wrought;
Thus on its sounding anvil shaped
  Each burning deed and thought!

King Robert of Sicily

H. W. LONGFELLOW

ROBERT of Sicily, brother of Pope Urbane
And Valmond, Emperor of Allemaine,
Apparelled in magnificent attire,
With retinue of many a knight and squire,

On St. John's eve, at vespers, proudly sat
And heard the priests chant the Magnificat.
And as he listened, o'er and o'er again
Repeated, like a burden or refrain,
He caught the words, " *Deposuit potentes*
De sede, et exaltavit humiles ";
And slowly lifting up his kingly head
He to a learned clerk beside him said,
" What mean these words? "   The clerk made answer
        meet,
" He has put down the mighty from their seat,
And has exalted them of low degree."
Thereat King Robert muttered scornfully,
" 'Tis well that such seditious words are sung
Only by priests and in the Latin tongue;
For unto priests and people be it known,
There is no power can push me from my throne! "
And leaning back, he yawned and fell asleep,
Lulled by the chant monotonous and deep.

When he awoke, it was already night;
The church was empty, and there was no light,
Save where the lamps, that glimmered few and faint,
Lighted a little space before some saint.
He started from his seat and gazed around,
But saw no living thing and heard no sound.
He groped towards the door, but it was locked;
He cried aloud, and listened, and then knocked,
And uttered awful threatenings and complaints,
And imprecations upon men and saints.
The sounds re-echoed from the roof and walls
As if dead priests were laughing in their stalls.

At length the sexton, hearing from without
The tumult of the knocking and the shout,

And thinking thieves were in the house of prayer,
Came with his lantern, asking, " Who is there? "
Half-choked with rage, King Robert fiercely said,
" Open: 'tis I, the King!　Art thou afraid? "
The frightened sexton, muttering, with a curse,
" This is some drunken vagabond, or worse! "
Turned the great key and flung the portal wide;
A man rushed by him at a single stride,
Haggard, half-naked, without hat or cloak,
Who neither turned, nor looked at him, nor spoke,
But leaped into the blackness of the night,
And vanished like a spectre from his sight.

Robert of Sicily, brother of Pope Urbane
And Valmond, Emperor of Allemaine,
Despoiled of his magnificent attire,
Bareheaded, breathless, and besprent with mire,
With sense of wrong and outrage desperate,
Strode on and thundered at the palace gate;
Rushed through the courtyard, thrusting in his rage
To right and left each seneschal and page,
And hurried up the broad and sounding stair,
His white face ghastly in the torches' glare.
From hall to hall he passed with breathless speed;
Voices and cries he heard, but did not heed,
Until at last he reached the banquet-room,
Blazing with light, and breathing with perfume.

There on the dais sat another king,
Wearing his robes, his crown, his signet-ring,
King Robert's self in features, form, and height,
But all transfigured with angelic light!
It was an Angel; and his presence there
With a divine effulgence filled the air,
An exaltation, piercing the disguise,
Though none the hidden Angel recognize.

A moment speechless, motionless, amazed,
The throneless monarch on the Angel gazed,
Who met his look of anger and surprise
With the divine compassion of his eyes;
Then said, " Who art thou? and why com'st thou
 here? "
To which King Robert answered, with a sneer,
" I am the King, and come to claim my own
From an impostor, who usurps my throne! "
And suddenly, at these audacious words,
Up sprang the angry guests, and drew their swords;
The Angel answered, with unruffled brow,
" Nay, not the King, but the King's Jester, thou
Henceforth shall wear the bells and scalloped cape,
And for thy counsellor shalt lead an ape;
Thou shalt obey my servants when they call,
And wait upon my henchmen in the hall! "

Deaf to King Robert's threats and cries and prayers,
They thrust him from the hall and down the stairs;
A group of tittering pages ran before,
And as they opened wide the folding door,
His heart failed, for he heard, with strange alarms,
The boisterous laughter of the men-at-arms,
And all the vaulted chamber roar and ring
With the mock plaudits of " Long live the King! "

Next morning, waking with the day's first beam,
He said within himself, " It was a dream! "
But the straw rustled as he turned his head,
There were the cap and bells beside his bed,
Around him rose the bare, discoloured walls,
Close by, the steeds were champing in their stalls,
And in the corner, a revolting shape,
Shivering and chattering sat the wretched ape.

It was no dream; the world he loved so much
Had turned to dust and ashes at his touch!
Days came and went; and now returned again
To Sicily the old Saturnian reign;
Under the Angel's governance benign
The happy island danced with corn and wine,
And deep within the mountain's burning breast
Enceladus, the giant, was at rest.
Meanwhile King Robert yielded to his fate,
Sullen and silent and disconsolate.
Dressed in the motley garb that Jesters wear,
With look bewildered and a vacant stare,
Close shaven above the ears, as monks are shorn,
By courtiers mocked, by pages laughed to scorn,
His only friend the ape, his only food
What others left,—he still was unsubdued.
And when the Angel met him on his way,
And half in earnest, half in jest, would say,
Sternly, though tenderly, that he might feel
The velvet scabbard held a sword of steel,
" Art thou the King? " the passion of his woe
Burst from him in resistless overflow,
And, lifting high his forehead, he would fling
The haughty answer back, " I am, I am the King! "

Almost three years were ended; when there came
Ambassadors of great repute and name
From Valmond, Emperor of Allemaine,
Unto King Robert, saying that Pope Urbane
By letter summoned them forthwith to come
On Holy Thursday to his city of Rome.
The Angel with great joy received his guests,
And gave them presents of embroidered vests,
And velvet mantles with rich ermine lined,
And rings and jewels of the rarest kind.

Then he departed with them o'er the sea
Into the lovely land of Italy,
Whose loveliness was more resplendent made
By the mere passing of that cavalcade,
With plumes, and cloaks, and housings, and the stir
Of jewelled bridle and of golden spur.

And lo! among the menials, in mock state,
Upon a piebald steed, with shambling gait,
His cloak of fox-tails flapping in the wind,
The solemn ape demurely perched behind,
King Robert rode, making huge merriment
In all the country towns through which they went.

The Pope received them with great pomp and blare
Of bannered trumpets, on Saint Peter's square.
Giving his benediction and embrace,
Fervent, and full of apostolic grace.
While with congratulations and with prayers
He entertained the Angel unawares,
Robert, the Jester, bursting through the crowd,
Into their presence rushed, and cried aloud,
" I am the King! Look, and behold in me
Robert, your brother, King of Sicily!
This man, who wears my semblance to your eyes,
Is an impostor in a king's disguise.
Do you not know me? does no voice within
Answer my cry, and say we are akin? "
The Pope in silence, but with troubled mien,
Gazed at the Angel's countenance serene:
The Emperor, laughing, said, " It is strange sport
To keep a madman for thy Fool at court! "
And the poor, baffled Jester in disgrace
Was hustled back among the populace.

In solemn state the Holy Week went by,
And Easter Sunday gleamed upon the sky;
The presence of the Angel, with its light,
Before the sun rose, made the city bright,
And with new fervour filled the hearts of men,
Who felt that Christ indeed had risen again.
Even the Jester, on his bed of straw,
With haggard eyes the unwonted splendour saw;
He felt within a power unfelt before,
And, kneeling humbly on his chamber floor,
He heard the rushing garments of the Lord
Sweep through the silent air, ascending heavenward.

And now the visit ending, and once more
Valmond returning to the Danube's shore,
Homeward the Angel journeyed, and again
The land was made resplendent with his train,
Flashing along the towns of Italy
Unto Salerno, and from thence by sea.
And when once more within Palermo's wall,
And, seated on the throne in his great hall,
He heard the Angelus from convent towers,
As if the better world conversed with ours,
He beckoned to King Robert to draw nigher,
And with a gesture bade the rest retire;
And when they were alone, the Angel said,
" Art thou the King? "   Then, bowing down his
        head,
King Robert crossed both hands upon his breast,
And meekly answered him: " Thou knowest best!
My sins as scarlet are; let me go hence,
And in some cloister's school of penitence,
Across those stones, that pave the way to heaven,
·Walk barefoot, till my guilty soul be shriven! "

The Angel smiled, and from his radiant face
A holy light illumined all the place,
And through the open window, loud and clear,
They heard the monks chant in the chapel near,
Above the stir and tumult of the street:
" He has put down the mighty from their seat,
And has exalted them of low degree! "
And through the chant a second melody
Rose like the throbbing of a single string:
" I am an Angel, and thou art the King! "

King Robert, who was standing near the throne,
Lifted his eyes, and lo! he was alone!
But all apparelled as in days of old,
With ermined mantle and with cloth of gold;
And when his courtiers came, they found him there
Kneeling upon the floor, absorbed in silent prayer.

Hiawatha's Childhood

H. W. LONGFELLOW

By the shores of Gitche Gumee,
By the shining Big Sea-Water,
Stood the wigwam of Nokomis,
Daughter of the Moon, Nokomis.
Dark behind it stood the forest,
Rose the black and gloomy pine-trees,
Rose the firs with cones upon them;
Bright before it beat the water,
Beat the shining Big Sea-Water.
Thus the wrinkled, old Nokomis
Nursed the little Hiawatha,
Rocked him in his linden cradle,

Bedded soft in moss and rushes.
Safely bound with reindeer sinews;
Stilled his fretful wail by saying,
" Hush; the naked bear will get thee! "
Lulled him into slumber, singing,
" Ewa-yea! my little owlet!
Who is this, that lights the wigwam?
With his great eyes lights the wigwam?
Ewa-yea! my little owlet! "

Many things Nokomis taught him
Of the stars that shine in heaven;
Showed him Ishkoodah, the comet,
Ishkoodah, with fiery tresses;
Showed the Death-Dance of the spirits,
Warriors with their plumes and war-clubs,
Flaring far away to northward
In the frosty nights of Winter;
Showed the broad, white road in heaven,
Pathway of the ghosts, the shadows,
Running straight across the heavens,
Crowded with the ghosts, the shadows.

At the door on Summer evenings
Sat the little Hiawatha;
Heard the whispering of the pine-trees,
Heard the lapping of the water,
Sounds of music, words of wonder;
" Minne-wawa! " said the pine-trees,
" Mudway-aushka! " said the water,
Saw the fire-fly, Wah-wah-taysee,
Flitting through the dusk of evening,
With the twinkle of his candle
Lighting up the brakes and bushes,
And he sang the song of children,
Sang the song Nokomis taught him;
" Wah-wah-taysee, little fire-fly,

Little, flitting, white-fire insect,
Little, dancing, white-fire creature,
Light me with your little candle,
Ere upon my bed I lay me,
Ere in sleep I close my eyelids! "

Saw the moon rise from the water,
Rippling, rounding from the water,
Saw the flecks and shadows on it.
Whispered, " What is that, Nokomis? "
And the good Nokomis answered:
" Once a warrior, very angry,
Seized his grandmother, and threw her
Up into the sky at midnight;
Right against the moon he threw her;
'Tis her body that you see there."

Saw the rainbow in the heaven,
In the eastern sky the rainbow,
Whispered, " What is that, Nokomis? "
And the good Nokomis answered:
" 'Tis the heaven of flowers you see there;
All the wild-flowers of the forest,
All the lilies of the prairie,
When on earth they fade and perish,
Blossom in that heaven above us."

When he heard the owls at midnight,
Hooting, laughing in the forest,
" What is that? " he cried in terror,
" What is that," he said, " Nokomis? "
And the good Nokomis answered:
" That is but the owl and owlet,
Talking in their native language,
Talking, scolding at each other."

Then the little Hiawatha
Learned of every bird its language,
Learned their names and all their secrets,

How they built their nests in Summer,
Where they hid themselves in Winter,
Talked with them whene'er he met them,
Called them " Hiawatha's Chickens ".
    Of all the beasts he learned the language,
Learned their names and all their secrets,
How the beavers built their lodges,
Where the squirrels hid their acorns,
How the reindeer ran so swiftly,
Why the rabbit was so timid,
Talked with them whene'er he met them,
Called them " Hiawatha's Brothers ".

Vision of Belshazzar

LORD BYRON

The King was on his throne,
    The Satraps thronged the hall:
A thousand bright lamps shone
    O'er that high festival.
A thousand cups of gold,
    In Judah deemed divine—
Jehovah's vessels hold
    The godless heathen's wine!

In that same hour and hall,
    The fingers of a hand
Came forth against the wall,
    And wrote as if on sand:
The fingers of a man;—
    A solitary hand
Along the letters ran,
    And traced them like a wand.

The monarch saw, and shook,
 And bade no more rejoice;
All bloodless waxed his look,
 And tremulous his voice.
" Let the men of lore appear,
 The wisest of the earth,
And expound the words of fear,
 Which mar our royal mirth."

Chaldea's seers are good,
 But here they have no skill;
And the unknown letters stood
 Untold and awful still.
And Babel's men of age
 Are wise and deep in lore;
But now they were not sage,
 They saw—but knew no more.

A captive in the land,
 A stranger and a youth,
He heard the king's command,
 He saw that writing's truth.
The lamps around were bright,
 The prophecy in view;
He read it on that night,—
 The morrow proved it true.

" Belshazzar's grave is made,
 His kingdom passed away,
He, in the balance weighed,
 Is light and worthless clay;
The shroud his robe of state,
 His canopy the stone;
The Mede is at his gate!
 The Persian on his throne! "

The Destruction of Sennacherib

LORD BYRON

THE Assyrian came down like a wolf on the fold,
And his cohorts were gleaming in purple and gold;
And the sheen of their spears was like stars on the sea,
When the blue wave rolls nightly on deep Galilee.

Like the leaves of the forest when Summer is green,
That host with their banners at sunset were seen;
Like the leaves of the forest when Autumn hath blown,
That host on the morrow lay wither'd and strown.

For the Angel of Death spread his wings on the blast,
And breath'd in the face of the foe as he pass'd;
And the eyes of the sleepers wax'd deadly and chill,
And their hearts but once heav'd, and for ever grew still!

And there lay the steed with his nostril all wide,
But through it there roll'd not the breath of his pride;
And the foam of his gasping lay white on the turf,
And cold as the spray of the rock-beating surf.

And there lay the rider distorted and pale,
With the dew on his brow, and the rust on his mail;
And the tents were all silent, the banners alone,
The lances unlifted, the trumpets unblown.

And the widows of Ashur are loud in their wail,
And the idols are broke in the temple of Baal;
And the might of the Gentile, unsmote by the sword,
Hath melted like snow in the glance of the Lord!

Waterloo

LORD BYRON

THERE was a sound of revelry by night,
And Belgium's capital had gather'd then
Her Beauty and her Chivalry, and bright
The lamps shone o'er fair women and brave men;
A thousand hearts beat happily; and when
Music arose with its voluptuous swell,
Soft eyes look'd love to eyes which spake again,
And all went merry as a marriage-bell;
But hush! hark! a deep sound strikes like a rising
    knell!

Did ye not hear it?—No; 'twas but the wind,
Or the car rattling o'er the stony street;
On with the dance! let joy be unconfined;
No sleep till morn, when Youth and Pleasure meet
To chase the glowing Hours with flying feet—
But, hark!—that heavy sound breaks in once more,
As if the clouds its echo would repeat;
And nearer, clearer, deadlier than before!
Arm! Arm! it is—it is—the cannon's opening roar!

Within a window'd niche of that high hall
Sate Brunswick's fated chieftain; he did hear
That sound the first amidst the festival,
And caught its tone with Death's prophetic ear;
And when they smiled because he deem'd it near,
His heart more truly knew that peal too well
Which stretch'd his father on a bloody bier,
And roused the vengeance blood alone could quell:
He rush'd into the field, and, foremost fighting, fell.

B   M.V.

Ah! then and there was hurrying to and fro,
And gathering tears, and tremblings of distress,
And cheeks all pale, which but an hour ago
Blush'd at the praise of their own loveliness;
And there were sudden partings, such as press
The life from out young hearts, and choking sighs
Which ne'er might be repeated; who could guess
If ever more should meet those mutual eyes,
Since upon night so sweet such awful morn could rise!

And there was mounting in hot haste: the steed,
The mustering squadron, and the clattering car,
Went pouring forward with impetuous speed,
And swiftly forming in the ranks of war;
And the deep thunder peal on peal afar;
And near, the beat of the alarming drum
Roused up the soldier ere the morning star;
While throng'd the citizens with terror dumb,
Or whispering, with white lips—" The foe! They come!
     they come! "

And wild and high the " Cameron's gathering " rose!
The war-note of Lochiel, which Albyn's hills
Have heard, and heard, too, have her Saxon foes:—
How in the noon of night that pibroch thrills,
Savage and shrill! But with the breath which fills
Their mountain-pipe, so fill the mountaineers
With the fierce native daring which instils
The stirring memory of a thousand years,
And Evan's, Donald's fame rings in each clansman's ears!

And Ardennes waves above them her green leaves,
Dewy with nature's tear-drops, as they pass,
Grieving, if aught inanimate e'er grieves,
Over the unreturning brave,—alas!

Ere evening to be trodden like the grass
Which now beneath them, but above shall grow
In its next verdure, when this fiery mass
Of living valour, rolling on the foe
And burning with high hope, shall moulder cold and
    low.

Last noon beheld them full of lusty life,
Last eve in Beauty's circle proudly gay,
The midnight brought the signal-sound of strife,
The morn the marshalling in arms,—the day
Battle's magnificently-stern array!
The thunder-clouds close o'er it, which when rent
The earth is cover'd thick with other clay,
Which her own clay shall cover, heap'd and pent,
Rider and horse,—friend, foe,—in one red burial blent!

After Blenheim

ROBERT SOUTHEY

It was a summer evening,
    Old Kaspar's work was done,
And he before his cottage door
    Was sitting in the sun;
And by him sported on the green
His little grandchild Wilhelmine.

She saw her brother Peterkin
    Roll something large and round
Which he beside the rivulet
    In playing there had found;
He came to ask what he had found
That was so large and smooth and round.

Old Kaspar took it from the boy
    Who stood expectant by;
And then the old man shook his head,
    And with a natural sigh
" 'Tis some poor fellow's skull," said he,
" Who fell in the great victory.

" I find them in the garden,
    For there's many here about;
And often when I go to plough
    The ploughshare turns them out.
For many thousand men," said he,
" Were slain in that great victory."

" Now tell us what 'twas all about,"
    Young Peterkin he cries;
And little Wilhelmine looks up
    With wonder-waiting eyes;
" Now tell us all about the war,
And what they fought each other for."

" It was the English," Kaspar cried,
    " Who put the French to rout;
But what they fought each other for
    I could not well make out.
But everybody said," quoth he,
" That 'twas a famous victory.

" My father lived at Blenheim then,
    Yon little stream hard by;
They burnt his dwelling to the ground,
    And he was forced to fly:
So with his wife and child he fled,
Nor had he where to rest his head.

" With fire and sword the country round
   Was wasted far and wide,
And many a childing mother then
   And new-born baby died:
But things like that, you know, must be
At every famous victory.

" They say it was a shocking sight
   After the field was won;
For many thousand bodies here
   Lay rotting in the sun:
But things like that, you know, must be
After a famous victory.

" Great praise the Duke of Marlbro' won
   And our good Prince Eugene ";
" Why, 'twas a very wicked thing! "
   Said little Wilhelmine;
" Nay . . . nay . . . my little girl," quoth he,
" It was a famous victory.

" And everybody praised the Duke
   Who this great fight did win."
" But what good came of it at last? "
   Quoth little Peterkin—
" Why, that I cannot tell," said he,
" But 'twas a famous victory."

The Inchcape Rock

ROBERT SOUTHEY

No stir in the air, no stir in the sea,
The ship was still as she could be,
Her sails from heaven received no motion,
Her keel was steady in the ocean.

Without either sign or sound of their shock,
The waves flowed over the Inchcape Rock;
So little they rose, so little they fell,
They did not move the Inchcape Bell.

The Abbot of Aberbrothok
Had placed that bell on the Inchcape Rock ;
On a buoy in the storm it floated and swung,
And over the waves its warning rung.

When the Rock was hid by the surge's swell,
The mariners heard the warning bell;
And then they knew the perilous Rock,
And blest the Abbot of Aberbrothok.

The sun in heaven was shining gay,
All things were joyful on that day;
The sea-birds screamed as they wheeled round,
And there was joyance in their sound.

The buoy of the Inchcape Bell was seen
A darker speck on the ocean green;
Sir Ralph the Rover walked his deck,
And he fixed his eye on the darker speck.

He felt the cheering power of spring,
It made him whistle, it made him sing;
His heart was mirthful to excess,
But the Rover's mirth was wickedness.

His eye was on the Inchcape float;
Quoth he, " My men, put out the boat,
And row me to the Inchcape Rock,
And I'll plague the Abbot of Aberbrothok."

The boat is lowered, the boatmen row,
And to the Inchcape Rock they go;
Sir Ralph bent over from the boat,
And he cut the bell from the Inchcape float.

Down sunk the bell with a gurgling sound,
The bubbles rose and burst around;
Quoth Sir Ralph, " The next who comes to the
     Rock
Won't bless the Abbot of Aberbrothok."

Sir Ralph the Rover sailed away,
He scoured the seas for many a day;
And now grown rich with plundered store,
He steers his course for Scotland's shore.

So thick a haze o'erspreads the sky
They cannot see the sun on high;
The wind hath blown a gale all day,
At evening it hath died away.

On the deck the Rover takes his stand,
So dark it is they see no land.
Quoth Sir Ralph, " It will be lighter soon,
For there is the dawn of the rising moon."

" Canst hear ", said one, " the breakers roar?
For methinks we should be near the shore."
" Now where we are I cannot tell,
But I wish I could hear the Inchcape Bell."

They hear no sound, the swell is strong;
Though the wind hath fallen they drift along,

Till the vessel strikes with a shivering shock,—
" O Christ! it is the Inchcape Rock! "

Sir Ralph the Rover tore his hair;
He cursed himself in his despair;
The waves rush in on every side,
The ship is sinking beneath the tide.

But even in his dying fear
One dreadful sound could the Rover hear,
A sound as if with the Inchcape Bell,
The Devil below was ringing his knell.

The Pipes of Lucknow

J. G. WHITTIER

PIPES of the misty moorlands,
   Voice of the glens and hills;
The droning of the torrents,
   The treble of the rills!
Not the braes of broom and heather,
   Nor the mountains dark with rain,
Nor maiden bower, nor border tower,
   Have heard your sweetest strain!

Dear to the Lowland reaper,
   And plaided mountaineer,—
To the cottage and the castle
   The Scottish pipes are dear;—
Sweet sounds the ancient pibroch
   O'er mountain, loch, and glade;
But the sweetest of all music
   The pipes at Lucknow played.

Day by day the Indian tiger
  Louder yelled, and nearer crept;
Round and round the jungle-serpent
  Near and nearer circles swept.
" Pray for rescue, wives and mothers,—
  Pray to-day! " the soldier said;
" To-morrow, death's between us
  And the wrong and shame we dread."

Oh, they listened, looked, and waited,
  Till their hope became despair;
And the sobs of low bewailing
  Filled the pauses of their prayer.
Then up spake a Scottish maiden,
  With her ear unto the ground:
" Dinna ye hear it?—dinna ye hear it?
  The pipes o' Havelock sound! "

Hushed the wounded man his groaning;
  Hushed the wife her little ones;
Alone they heard the drum-roll
  And the roar of Sepoy guns.
But to sounds of home and childhood
  The Highland ear was true;—
As her mother's cradle-crooning
  The mountain pipes she knew.

Like the march of soundless music
  Through the vision of the seer,
More of feeling than of hearing,
  Of the heart than of the ear,
She knew the droning pibroch,
  She knew the Campbell's call:
" Hark! hear ye no' MacGregor's,—
  The grandest o' them all! "

Oh, they listened, dumb and breathless,
    And they caught the sound at last;
Faint and far beyond the Goomtee
    Rose and fell the piper's blast!
Then a burst of wild thanksgiving
    Mingled woman's voice and man's;
" God be praised!—the march of Havelock!
    The piping of the clans! "

Louder, nearer, fierce as vengeance,
    Sharp and shrill as swords at strife,
Came the wild MacGregor's clan-call,
    Stinging all the air to life,
But when the far-off dust-cloud
    To plaided legions grew,
Full tenderly and blithesomely
    The pipes of rescue blew!

Round the silver domes of Lucknow,
    Moslem mosque and Pagan shrine,
Breathed the air to Britons dearest,
    The air of " Auld Lang Syne ".
O'er the cruel roll of war-drums
    Rose that sweet and homelike strain;
And the tartan clove the turban,
    As the Goomtee cleaves the plain.

Dear to the corn-land reaper
    And plaided mountaineer,—
To the cottage and the castle
    The piper's song is dear.
Sweet sounds the Gaelic pibroch
    O'er mountain, glen, and glade;
But the sweetest of all music
    The pipes at Lucknow played!

The Song of the Heavens

JOSEPH ADDISON

THE spacious firmament on high,
With all the blue ethereal sky,
And spangled heavens, a shining frame,
Their great Original proclaim.
Th' unwearied Sun from day to day
Does his Creator's power display,
And publishes to every land
The work of an Almighty hand.

Soon as the evening shades prevail,
The Moon takes up the wondrous tale,
And nightly to the listening Earth
Repeats the story of her birth;
Whilst all the stars that round her burn,
And all the planets in their turn,
Confirm the tidings as they roll,
And spread the truth from pole to pole.

What though in solemn silence all
Move round the dark terrestrial ball;
What though nor real voice nor sound
Amidst their radiant orbs be found?
In Reason's ear they all rejoice,
And utter forth a glorious voice,
For ever singing as they shine,
" The Hand that made us is divine ".

The Camel's Hump

RUDYARD KIPLING

THE Camel's hump is an ugly lump
   Which well you may see at the Zoo;
But uglier yet is the hump we get
   From having too little to do.

Kiddies and grown-ups too-oo-oo,
If we haven't enough to do-oo-oo,
   We get the hump—
   Cameelious hump—
The hump that is black and blue!

We climb out of bed with a frouzly head
   And a snarly-yarly voice;
We shiver and scowl, and we grunt and we growl
   At our bath and our boots and our toys;

And there ought to be a corner for me
(And I know there is one for you)
   When we get the hump—
   Cameelious hump—
The hump that is black and blue!

The cure for this ill is not to sit still,
   Or frowst with a book by the fire;
But to take a large hoe and a shovel also,
   And dig till you gently perspire;

And then you will find that the sun and the wind,
And the Djinn of the garden too,
   Have lifted the hump—
   The horrible hump—
The hump that is black and blue!

I get it as well as you-oo-oo
If I haven't enough to do-oo-oo,
   We all get the hump—
   Cameelious hump—
Kiddies and grown-ups too!

A Smuggler's Song

RUDYARD KIPLING

If you wake at midnight, and hear a horse's feet,
Don't go drawing back the blind, or looking in the street,
Them that ask no questions isn't told a lie.
Watch the wall, my darling, while the Gentlemen go by!
     Five and twenty ponies,
     Trotting through the dark—
     Brandy for the Parson,
     'Baccy for the Clerk;
Laces for a lady, letters for a spy,
And watch the wall, my darling, while the Gentlemen go
    by!

Running round the woodlump if you chance to find
Little barrels, roped and tarred, all full of brandy-wine,
Don't you shout to come and look, nor use 'em for your
    play.
Put the brishwood back again—and they'll be gone next
    day!

If you see the stable-door setting open wide;
If you see a tired horse lying down inside;
If your mother mends a coat cut about and tore;
If the lining's wet and warm—don't you ask no more!

If you meet King George's men, dressed in blue and red,
You be careful what you say, and mindful what is said.
If they call you " pretty maid ", and chuck you 'neath
    the chin,
Don't you tell where no one is, nor yet where no one's
    been!

Knocks and footsteps round the house—whistles after
    dark—
You've no call for running out till the house-dogs bark.
Trusty's here, and *Pincher's* here, and see how dumb they
    lie—
They don't fret to follow when the Gentlemen go by!

If you do as you've been told, 'likely there's a chance,
You'll be give a dainty doll, all the way from France,
With a cap of Valenciennes, and a velvet hood—
A present from the Gentlemen, along o' being good!
        Five and twenty ponies,
        Trotting through the dark—
        Brandy for the Parson,
        'Baccy for the Clerk.
Them that asks no questions isn't told a lie—
Watch the wall, my darling, while the Gentlemen go by!

The Glove and the Lions

LEIGH HUNT

KING FRANCIS was a hearty king, and loved a royal sport,
And one day, as his lions strove, sat looking on the court;
The nobles filled the benches round, the ladies by their
    side,
And 'mongst them Count de Lorge, with one he hoped to
    make his bride;

And truly 'twas a gallant thing, to see the crowning
 show,
Valour and love, and a king above, and the royal beasts
 below.

Ramped and roared the lions, with horrid laughing jaws;
They bit, they glared, gave blows like beams, a wind
 went with their paws.
With wallowing might and stifled roar they rolled one on
 another,
Till all the pit, with sand and mane, was in a thund'rous
 smother;
The bloody foam above the bars came whizzing through
 the air;
Said Francis then, " Good gentlemen, we're better here
 than there! "

De Lorge's love o'erheard the king, a beauteous lively
 dame,
With smiling lips, and sharp bright eyes, which always
 seemed the same:
She thought, the Count, my lover, is as brave as brave
 can be;
He surely would do desperate things to show his love of
 me!
King, ladies, lovers, all look on; the chance is wondrous
 fine;
I'll drop my glove to prove his love; great glory will be
 mine!

She dropped her glove to prove his love: then looked on
 him and smiled;
He bowed, and in a moment leaped among the lions
 wild!

The leap was quick; return was quick; he soon regained
    his place,
Then threw the glove, but not with love, right in the
    lady's face!
" Well done! " cried Francis, " bravely done! " and he
    rose from where he sat:
" No love," quoth he, " but vanity, sets love a task like
    that! "

King John and the Abbot of Canterbury

ANONYMOUS

An ancient story I'll tell you anon
Of a notable prince that was called King John;
And he ruled England with main and with might,
For he did great wrong and maintain'd little right.

And I'll tell you a story, a story so merry,
Concerning the Abbot of Canterbury;
How for his house-keeping, and high renown,
They rode post for him to fair London town.

A hundred men, the king did hear say,
The abbot kept in his house every day;
And fifty gold chains, without any doubt,
In velvet coats waited the abbot about.

How now, father abbot, I hear it of thee,
Thou keepest a far better house than me,
And, for thy house-keeping and high renown,
I fear thou work'st treason against my crown.

My liege, quo' the abbot, I would it were known,
I never spend nothing but what is my own;
And I trust your grace will do me no dere
For spending of my own true-gotten gear.

Yes, yes, father abbot, thy fault it is high,
And now for the same thou needest must die:
For except thou canst answer me questions three,
Thy head shall be smitten from thy body.

And first, quo' the king, when I'm in this stead,
With my crown of gold so fair on my head,
Among all my liege-men so noble of birth,
Thou must tell me to one penny what I am worth.

Secondly, tell me, without any doubt,
How soon I may ride the whole world about.
And at the third question thou must not shrink,
But tell me here truly what I do think.

O, these are hard questions for my shallow wit,
Nor I cannot answer your grace as yet:
But if you will give me but three weeks' space,
I'll do my endeavour to answer your grace.

Now three weeks' space to thee will I give,
And that is the longest time thou hast to live;
For if thou dost not answer my questions three,
Thy lands and thy livings are forfeit to me.

Away rode the abbot all sad at that word,
And he rode to Cambridge and Oxenford;
But never a doctor there was so wise
That could with his learning an answer devise.

M.V.

Then home rode the abbot of comfort so cold,
And he met his shepherd a-going to fold:
How now, my lord abbot, you are welcome home;
What news do you bring us from good King John?

Sad news, sad news, shepherd, I must give:
That I have but three days more to live;
For if I do not answer him questions three,
My head will be smitten from my body.

The first is to tell him there in that stead,
With his crown of gold so fair on his head,
Among all his liege-men so noble of birth,
To within one penny of what he is worth.

The second, to tell him, without any doubt,
How soon he may ride this whole world about:
And at the third question I must not shrink,
But tell him there truly what he does think.

Now cheer up, sir abbot! Did you never hear yet,
That a fool he may learn a wise man wit?
Lend me horse, and your serving-men, and apparel,
And I'll ride to London to answer your quarrel.

Nay frown not, if it hath been told unto me,
I am like your lordship as ever may be:
And if you will but lend me your gown,
There is none shall know us at fair London town.

Now horses, and serving-men thou shalt have,
With sumptuous array most gallant and brave,
With crozier, and mitre, and rochet, and cope,
Fit to appear 'fore our father the pope.

Now welcome, sir abbot, the king he did say,
'Tis well thou'rt come back to keep thy day;
For if thou canst answer my questions three,
Thy life and thy living both saved shall be.

And first when thou seest me here in this stead,
With my crown of gold so fair on my head,
Among all my liege-men so noble of birth,
Tell me to one penny what I am worth.

" For thirty pence our Saviour was sold
Among the false Jews, as I have been told;
And twenty-nine is the worth of thee,
For I think thou'rt *one* penny worser than he."

The king he laughed, and swore by St. Bittel:
I did not think I had been worth so little!
—Now secondly tell me, without any doubt,
How soon I may ride this whole world about.

" You must rise with the sun, and ride with the same,
Until the next morning he riseth again;
And then your grace need not make any doubt,
But in twenty-four hours you'll ride it about."

The king he laughed, and swore by St. John:
I did not think I could do it so soon!
—Now from the third question thou must not shrink,
But tell me here truly what I do think.

" Yea, that shall I do, and make your grace merry:
You think I'm the abbot of Canterbury;
But I'm his poor shepherd, as plain you may see,
That am come to beg pardon for him and for me."

The king he laughed, and swore by the mass,
I'll make thee lord abbot this day in his place!
" Now nay, my liege, be not in such speed,
For alack I can neither write nor read."

Four nobles a week then I will give thee,
For this merry jest thou hast shown unto me;
And tell the old abbot, when thou comest home,
Thou hast brought him a pardon from good King John.

The Priest and the Mulberry Tree

THOMAS LOVE PEACOCK

DID you hear of the curate who mounted his mare,
And merrily trotted along to the fair?
Of creature more tractable none ever heard:
In the height of her speed she would stop at a word;
But again with a word, when the curate said, " Hey,"
She put forth her mettle and gallop'd away.

As near to the gates of the city he rode,
While the sun of September all brilliantly glow'd,
The good priest discover'd, with eyes of desire,
A mulberry tree in a hedge of wild brier;
On boughs long and lofty, in many a green shoot,
Hung, large, black, and glossy, the beautiful fruit.

The curate was hungry and thirsty to boot;
He shrank from the thorns, though he longed for the
        fruit;
With a word he arrested his courser's keen speed,
And he stood up erect on the back of his steed;
On the saddle he stood while the creature stood still,
And he gather'd the fruit till he took his good fill.

" Sure never ", he thought, " was a creature so rare,
So docile, so true, as my excellent mare;
Lo, here now I stand ", and he gazed all around,
" As safe and as steady as if on the ground;
Yet how had it been, if some traveller this way,
Had, dreaming no mischief, but chanced to cry ' Hey '? "

He stood with his head in the mulberry tree,
And he spoke out aloud in his fond revery;
At the sound of the word the good mare made a push,
And down went the priest in the wild-brier bush.
He remembered too late, on his thorny green bed,
Much that well may be thought cannot wisely be said.

The Diverting History of John Gilpin

WILLIAM COWPER

JOHN GILPIN was a citizen
    Of credit and renown,
A train-band captain eke was he
    Of famous London town.

John Gilpin's spouse said to her dear,
    " Though wedded we have been
These twice ten tedious years, yet we
    No holiday have seen.

" To-morrow is our wedding-day,
    And we will then repair
Unto the Bell at Edmonton,
    All in a chaise and pair.

" My sister, and my sister's child,
    Myself, and children three,
Will fill the chaise; so you must ride
    On horseback after we."

He soon replied, " I do admire
    Of womankind but one,
And you are she, my dearest dear,
    Therefore it shall be done.

" I am a linen-draper bold,
    As all the world doth know,
And my good friend the calender
    Will lend his horse to go."

Quoth Mrs. Gilpin, " That's well said;
    And for that wine is dear,
We will be furnished with our own,
    Which is both bright and clear."

John Gilpin kissed his loving wife;
    O'erjoyed was he to find,
That though on pleasure she was bent,
    She had a frugal mind.

The morning came, the chaise was brought,
    But yet was not allowed
To drive up to the door, lest all
    Should say that she was proud.

So three doors off the chaise was stayed,
    Where they did all get in;
Six precious souls, and all agog
    To dash through thick and thin.

Smack went the whip, round went the wheels,
  Were never folk so glad,
The stones did rattle underneath,
  As if Cheapside were mad.

John Gilpin at his horse's side
  Seized fast the flowing mane,
And up he got, in haste to ride,
  But soon came down again;

For saddle-tree scarce reached had he,
  His journey to begin,
When, turning round his head, he saw
  Three customers come in.

So down he came; for loss of time,
  Although it grieved him sore,
Yet loss of pence, full well he knew,
  Would trouble him much more.

'Twas long before the customers
  Were suited to their mind,
When Betty screaming came down stairs,
  " The wine is left behind! "

" Good lack! " quoth he—" yet bring it me,
  My leathern belt likewise,
In which I bear my trusty sword,
  When I do exercise."

Now Mistress Gilpin (careful soul!)
  Had two stone bottles found,
To hold the liquor that she loved,
  And keep it safe and sound.

Each bottle had a curling ear,
    Through which the belt he drew,
And hung a bottle on each side,
    To make his balance true.

Then over all, that he might be
    Equipped from top to toe,
His long red cloak, well brushed and neat,
    He manfully did throw.

Now see him mounted once again
    Upon his nimble steed,
Full slowly pacing o'er the stones,
    With caution and good heed.

But finding soon a smoother road
    Beneath his well-shod feet,
The snorting beast began to trot,
    Which galled him in his seat.

So, " Fair and softly," John he cried,
    But John he cried in vain;
That trot became a gallop soon,
    In spite of curb and rein.

So stooping down, as needs he must
    Who cannot sit upright,
He grasped the mane with both his hands,
    And eke with all his might.

His horse, who never in that sort
    Had handled been before,
What thing upon his back had got
    Did wonder more and more.

Away went Gilpin, neck or nought;
    Away went hat and wig;
He little dreamt, when he set out,
    Of running such a rig.

The wind did blow, the cloak did fly,
    Like streamer long and gay,
Till, loop and button failing both,
    At last it flew away.

Then might all people well discern
    The bottles he had slung;
A bottle swinging at each side,
    As hath been said or sung.

The dogs did bark, the children screamed,
    Up flew the windows all;
And every soul cried out, " Well done! "
    As loud as he could bawl.

Away went Gilpin—who but he?
    His fame soon spread around;
" He carries weight! "   " He rides a race! "
    " 'Tis for a thousand pound! "

And still, as fast as he drew near,
    'Twas wonderful to view,
How in a trice the turnpike-men
    Their gates wide open threw.

And now, as he went bowing down
    His reeking head full low,
The bottles twain behind his back
    Were shattered at a blow.

Down ran the wine into the road,
    Most piteous to be seen,
Which made his horse's flanks to smoke
    As they had basted been.

But still he seemed to carry weight,
    With leathern girdle braced;
For all might see the bottle-necks
    Still dangling at his waist.

Thus all through merry Islington
    These gambols he did play,
Until he came unto the Wash
    Of Edmonton so gay;

And there he threw the Wash about
    On both sides of the way,
Just like unto a trundling mop,
    Or a wild goose at play.

At Edmonton his loving wife
    From the balcony espied
Her tender husband, wondering much
    To see how he did ride.

" Stop, stop, John Gilpin!—Here's the house! "
    They all at once did cry;
" The dinner waits, and we are tired ";—
    Said Gilpin—" So am I! "

But yet his horse was not a whit
    Inclined to tarry there!
For why?—his owner had a house
    Full ten miles off, at Ware.

So like an arrow swift he flew,
   Shot by an archer strong;
So did he fly—which brings me to
   The middle of my song.

Away went Gilpin out of breath,
   And sore against his will,
Till at his friend the calender's
   His horse at last stood still.

The calender, amazed to see
   His neighbour in such trim,
Laid down his pipe, flew to the gate,
   And thus accosted him:

" What news? what news? your tidings tell;
   Tell me you must and shall—
Say why bareheaded you are come,
   Or why you come at all? "

Now Gilpin had a pleasant wit,
   And loved a timely joke;
And thus unto the calender
   In merry guise he spoke:

" I came because your horse would come,
   And, if I well forbode,
My hat and wig will soon be here,—
   They are upon the road."

The calender, right glad to find
   His friend in merry pin,
Returned him not a single word,
   But to the house went in;

Whence straight he came with hat and wig;
   A wig that flowed behind,
A hat not much the worse for wear,
   Each comely in its kind.

He held them up, and in his turn
   Thus showed his ready wit,
" My head is twice as big as yours,
   They therefore needs must fit.

" But let me scrape the dirt away
   That hangs upon your face;
And stop and eat, for well you may
   Be in a hungry case."

Said John, " It is my wedding-day,
   And all the world would stare,
If wife should dine at Edmonton,
   And I should dine at Ware."

So turning to his horse, he said,
   " I am in haste to dine;
'Twas for your pleasure you came here,
   You shall go back for mine."

Ah, luckless speech, and bootless boast!
   For which he paid full dear;
For, while he spake, a braying ass
   Did sing most loud and clear;

Whereat his horse did snort, as he
   Had heard a lion roar,
And galloped off with all his might,
   As he had done before.

Away went Gilpin, and away
   Went Gilpin's hat and wig:
He lost them sooner than at first;
   For why?—they were too big.

Now Mistress Gilpin when she saw
   Her husband posting down
Into the country far away,
   She pulled out half a crown;

And thus unto the youth she said
   That drove them to the Bell,
" This shall be yours, when you bring back
   My husband safe and well."

The youth did ride, and soon did meet
   John coming back amain:
Whom in a trice he tried to stop,
   By catching at his rein;

But not performing what he meant,
   And gladly would have done,
The frighted steed he frighted more,
   And made him faster run.

Away went Gilpin, and away
   Went postboy at his heels,
The postboy's horse right glad to miss
   The lumbering of the wheels.

Six gentlemen upon the road,
   Thus seeing Gilpin fly,
With postboy scampering in the rear,
   They raised the hue and cry;

" Stop thief! stop thief!—a highwayman! "
    Not one of them was mute;
And all and each that passed that way
    Did join in the pursuit.

And now the turnpike gates again
    Flew open in short space;
The toll-men thinking, as before,
    That Gilpin rode a race.

And so he did, and won it too,
    For he got first to town;
Nor stopped till where he had got up
    He did again get down.

Now let us sing, Long live the king!
    And Gilpin, long live he!
And when he next doth ride abroad
    May I be there to see!

Ivry

A Song of the Huguenots

LORD MACAULAY

Now glory to the Lord of Hosts, from whom all glories are!
And glory to our Sovereign Liege, King Henry of
    Navarre!
Now let there be the merry sound of music and of dance,
Through thy corn-fields green, and sunny vines, oh
    pleasant land of France!
And thou, Rochelle, our own Rochelle, proud city of the
    waters,
Again let rapture light the eyes of all thy mourning
    daughters.

As thou wert constant in our ills, be joyous in our joy,
For cold, and stiff, and still are they who wrought thy
walls annoy.
Hurrah! Hurrah! a single field hath turned the chance
of war,
Hurrah! Hurrah! for Ivry, and Henry of Navarre.

Oh! how our hearts were beating when, at the dawn of
day,
We saw the army of the League drawn out in long array;
With all its priest-led citizens, and all its rebel peers,
And Appenzel's stout infantry, and Egmont's Flemish
spears.
There rode the brood of false Lorraine, the curses of our
land;
And dark Mayenne was in the midst, a truncheon in his
hand:
And, as we looked on them, we thought of Seine's
empurpled flood,
And good Coligny's hoary hair all dabbled with his blood;
And we cried unto the living God, who rules the fate of war,
To fight for His own holy name, and Henry of Navarre.

The King is come to marshal us, in all his armour drest,
And he has bound a snow-white plume upon his gallant
crest.
He looked upon his people, and a tear was in his eye;
He looked upon the traitors, and his glance was stern and
high.
Right graciously he smiled on us, as rolled from wing to
wing,
Down all our line, a deafening shout, " God save our
Lord the King!"
" An if my standard-bearer fall, as fall full well he may,
For never saw I promise yet of such a bloody fray,

Press where ye see my white plume shine, amidst the
     ranks of war,
And be your oriflamme to-day the helmet of Navarre."

Hurrah! the foes are moving. Hark to the mingled din
Of fife, and steed, and trump, and drum, and roaring
     culverin.
The fiery Duke is pricking fast across Saint André's plain,
With all the hireling chivalry of Guelders and Almayne.
Now by the lips of those ye love, fair gentlemen of France,
Charge for the golden lilies,—upon them with the lance!
A thousand spurs are striking deep, a thousand spears in rest,
A thousand knights are pressing close behind the snow-
     white crest;
And in they burst, and on they rushed, while, like a
     guiding star,
Amidst the thickest carnage blazed the helmet of Navarre.

Now, God be praised, the day is ours. Mayenne hath
     turned his rein.
D'Aumale hath cried for quarter. The Flemish count is
     slain.
Their ranks are breaking like thin clouds before a Biscay
     gale;
The field is heaped with bleeding steeds, and flags, and
     cloven mail.
And then we thought on vengeance, and, all along our van,
" Remember Saint Bartholomew! " was passed from man
     to man.
But out spake gentle Henry, " No Frenchman is my foe:
Down, down with every foreigner, but let your brethren
     go."
Oh! was there ever such a knight, in friendship or in war,
As our Sovereign Lord, King Henry, the soldier of
     Navarre?

Right well fought all the Frenchmen who fought for
      France to-day;
And many a lordly banner God gave them for a prey.
But we of the religion have borne us best in fight;
And the good Lord of Rosny has ta'en the cornet white.
Our own true Maximilian the cornet white hath ta'en,
The cornet white with crosses black, the flag of false
      Lorraine.
Up with it high; unfurl it wide; that all the host may
      know
How God hath humbled the proud house which wrought
      His church such woe.
Then on the ground, while trumpets sound their loudest
      point of war,
Fling the red shreds, a footcloth meet for Henry of
      Navarre.

Ho! maidens of Vienna; Ho! matrons of Lucerne;
Weep, weep, and rend your hair for those who never
      shall return.
Ho! Philip, send, for charity, thy Mexican pistoles,
That Antwerp monks may sing a mass for thy poor spear-
      men's souls.
Ho! gallant nobles of the League, look that your arms be
      bright;
Ho! burghers of Saint Genevieve, keep watch and ward
      to-night.
For our God hath crushed the tyrant, our God hath
      raised the slave,
And mocked the counsel of the wise, and the valour of the
      brave.
Then glory to His holy name, from whom all glories are;
And glory to our Sovereign Lord, King Henry of Navarre.

The Battle of Naseby

By Obadiah-bind-their-kings-in-chains-and-their-nobles-with-links-of-iron, Sergeant in Ireton's Regiment

LORD MACAULAY

Oн! wherefore come ye forth, in triumph from the North,
    With your hands, and your feet, and your raiment all
        red?
And wherefore doth your rout send forth a joyous shout?
    And whence be the grapes of the wine-press which ye
        tread?

Oh! evil was the root, and bitter was the fruit,
    And crimson was the juice of the vintage that we trod;
For we trampled on the throng of the haughty and the
        strong,
    Who sate in the high places, and slew the saints of
        God.

It was about the noon of a glorious day of June,
    That we saw their banners dance, and their cuirasses
        shine,
And the Man of Blood was there, with his long essenced
        hair,
    And Astley, and Sir Marmaduke, and Rupert of the
        Rhine.

Like a servant of the Lord, with his Bible and his sword
    The General rode along us to form us to the fight,
When a murmuring sound broke out, and swell'd into a
        shout,
    Among the godless horsemen upon the tyrant's right.

And hark! like the roar of the billows on the shore,
 The cry of battle rises along their charging line!
For God! for the Cause! for the Church! for the Laws!
 For Charles King of England and Rupert of the Rhine!

The furious German comes, with his clarions and his
  drums,
 His bravoes of Alsatia, and pages of Whitehall;
They are bursting on our flanks. Grasp your pikes, close
  your ranks;
 For Rupert never comes but to conquer or to fall.

They are here! They rush on! We are broken! We
  are gone!
 Our left is borne before them like stubble on the blast.
O Lord, put forth thy might! O Lord, defend the right!
 Stand back to back, in God's name, and fight it to the last.

Stout Skippon hath a wound; the centre hath given
  ground:
 Hark! hark!—What means the trampling of horsemen
  on our rear?
Whose banner do I see, boys? 'Tis he, thank God, 'tis
  he, boys,
 Bear up another minute: brave Oliver is here.

Their heads all stooping low, their points all in a row,
 Like a whirlwind on the trees, like a deluge on the dykes,
Our cuirassiers have burst on the ranks of the Accurst,
 And at a shock have scattered the forest of his pikes.

Fast, fast, the gallants ride, in some safe nook to hide
 Their coward heads, predestined to rot on Temple Bar;
And he—he turns, he flies:—shame on those cruel eyes
 That bore to look on torture, and dare not look on war.

Ho! comrades, scour the plain; and, ere ye strip the
  slain,
 First give another stab to make your search secure,
Then shake from sleeves and pockets their broad-pieces
  and lockets,
 The tokens of the wanton, the plunder of the poor.

Fools! your doublets shone with gold, and your hearts
  were gay and bold,
 When you kissed your lily hands to your lemans to-day;
And to-morrow shall the fox, from her chambers in the
  rocks,
 Lead forth her tawny cubs to howl above the prey.

Where be your tongues that late mocked at heaven and
  hell and fate,
 And the fingers that once were so busy with your blades,
Your perfum'd satin clothes, your catches and your oaths,
 Your stage-plays and your sonnets, your diamonds and
  your spades?

Down, down, forever down with the mitre and the crown,
 With the Belial of the Court and the Mammon of the
  Pope;
There is woe in Oxford halls; there is wail in Durham's
  Stalls:
 The Jesuit smites his bosom; the Bishop rends his cope.

And She of the seven hills shall mourn her children's ills,
 And tremble when she thinks on the edge of England's
  sword;
And the Kings of earth in fear shall shudder when they
  hear
 What the hand of God hath wrought for the Houses
  and the Word.

Horatius

LORD MACAULAY

Lars Porsena of Clusium
    By the Nine Gods he swore
That the great house of Tarquin
    Should suffer wrong no more.
By the Nine Gods he swore it,
    And named a trysting day,
And bade his messengers ride forth,
East and west and south and north,
    To summon his array.

East and west and south and north
    The messengers ride fast,
And tower and town and cottage
    Have heard the trumpet's blast.
Shame on the false Etruscan
    Who lingers in his home,
When Porsena of Clusium
    Is on the march for Rome.

And now hath every city
    Sent up her tale of men;
The foot are fourscore thousand,
    The horse are thousands ten:
Before the gates of Sutrium
    Is met the great array.
A proud man was Lars Porsena
    Upon the trysting day.

But by the yellow Tiber
    Was tumult and affright:
From all the spacious champaign
    To Rome men took their flight.

A mile around the city,
  The throng stopped up the ways;
A fearful sight it was to see
  Through two long nights and days.

Now, from the rock Tarpeian,
  Could the wan burghers spy
The line of blazing villages
  Red in the midnight sky.
The Fathers of the City,
  They sat all night and day,
For every hour some horseman came
  With tidings of dismay.

I wis, in all the Senate,
  There was no heart so bold,
But sore it ached and fast it beat,
  When that ill news was told.
Forthwith up rose the Consul,
  Up rose the Fathers all;
In haste they girded up their gowns,
  And hied them to the wall.

They held a council standing
  Before the River-Gate;
Short time was there, ye well may guess,
  For musing or debate.
Out spake the Consul roundly:
  "The bridge must straight go down;
For, since Janiculum is lost,
  Naught else can save the town."

Just then a scout came flying,
  All wild with haste and fear;
"To arms! to arms! Sir Consul:
  Lars Porsena is here."

On the low hills to westward
  The Consul fixed his eye,
And saw the swarthy storm of dust
  Rise fast along the sky.

And nearer fast and nearer
  Doth the red whirlwind come;
And louder still and still more loud,
From underneath that rolling cloud,
Is heard the trumpet's war-note proud,
  The trampling, and the hum.
And plainly and more plainly
  Now through the gloom appears,
Far to left and far to right,
In broken gleams of dark-blue light,
The long array of helmets bright,
  The long array of spears.

But the Consul's brow was sad,
  And the Consul's speech was low,
And darkly looked he at the wall,
  And darkly at the foe.
" Their van will be upon us
  Before the bridge goes down;
And if they once may win the bridge,
  What hope to save the town? "

Then out spake brave Horatius,
  The Captain of the Gate:
" To every man upon this earth
  Death cometh soon or late.
And how can man die better
  Than facing fearful odds,
For the ashes of his fathers,
  And the temples of his Gods?

" Hew down the bridge, Sir Consul,
    With all the speed ye may;
I, with two more to help me,
    Will hold the foe in play.
In yon strait path a thousand
    May well be stopped by three.
Now who will stand on either hand,
    And keep the bridge with me? "

Then out spake Spurius Lartius;
    A Ramnian proud was he:
" Lo, I will stand at thy right hand,
    And keep the bridge with thee."
And out spake strong Herminius;
    Of Titian blood was he:
" I will abide on thy left side,
    And keep the bridge with thee."

" Horatius," quoth the Consul,
    " As thou sayest, so let it be."
And straight against that great array
    Forth went the dauntless Three.
For Romans in Rome's quarrel
    Spared neither land nor gold,
Nor son nor wife, nor limb nor life,
    In the brave days of old.

Now while the Three were tightening
    Their harness on their backs,
The Consul was the foremost man
    To take in hand an axe:
And Fathers mixed with Commons,
    Seized hatchet, bar, and crow,
And smote upon the planks above,
    And loosed the props below.

Meanwhile the Tuscan army,
   Right glorious to behold,
Came flashing back the noonday light,
Rank behind rank, like surges bright
   Of a broad sea of gold.
Four hundred trumpets sounded
   A peal of warlike glee,
As that great host, with measured tread,
And spears advanced, and ensigns spread,
Rolled slowly towards the bridge's head,
   Where stood the dauntless Three.

The Three stood calm and silent
   And looked upon the foes,
And a great shout of laughter
   From all the vanguard rose:
And forth three chiefs came spurring
   Before that deep array;
To earth they sprang, their swords they drew,
And lifted high their shields, and flew
   To win the narrow way:

Aunus from green Tifernum,
   Lord of the Hill of Vines;
And Seius, whose eight hundred slaves
   Sicken in Ilva's mines;
And Picus, long to Clusium
   Vassal in peace and war,
Who led to fight his Umbrian powers
From that great crag where, girt with towers,
The fortress of Nequinum lowers
   O'er the pale waves of Nar.

c*

Stout Lartius hurled down Aunus
  Into the stream beneath:
Herminius struck at Seius,
  And clove him to the teeth:
At Picus brave Horatius
  Darted one fiery thrust,
And the proud Umbrian's gilded arms
  Clashed in the bloody dust.

Then Ocnus of Falerii
  Rushed on the Roman Three;
And Lausulus of Urgo,
  The rover of the sea;
And Aruns of Volsinium,
  Who slew the great wild boar,
The great wild boar that had his den
Amidst the reeds of Cosa's fen,
And wasted fields, and slaughtered men,
  Along Albinia's shore.

Herminius smote down Aruns:
  Lartius laid Ocnus low:
Right to the heart of Lausulus
  Horatius sent a blow.
" Lie there," he cried, " fell pirate!
  No more, aghast and pale,
From Ostia's walls the crowd shall mark
The track of thy destroying bark;
No more Campania's hinds shall fly
To woods and caverns when they spy
  Thy thrice accursed sail."

But now no sound of laughter
  Was heard among the foes.
A wild and wrathful clamour
  From all the vanguard rose.

Six spears' length from the entrance
   Halted that deep array,
And for a space no man came forth
   To win the narrow way.

But hark! the cry is Astur:
   And lo! the ranks divide;
And the great Lord of Luna
   Comes with his stately stride.
Upon his ample shoulders
   Clangs loud the fourfold shield,
And in his hand he shakes the brand
   Which none but he can wield.

He smiled on those bold Romans
   A smile serene and high;
He eyed the flinching Tuscans,
   And scorn was in his eye.
Quoth he, " The she-wolf's litter
   Stand savagely at bay:
But will ye dare to follow,
   If Astur clears the way? "

Then, whirling up his broadsword
   With both hands to the height,
He rushed against Horatius,
   And smote with all his might.
With shield and blade Horatius
   Right deftly turned the blow.
The blow, though turned, came yet too nigh;
It missed his helm, but gashed his thigh:
The Tuscans raised a joyful cry
   To see the red blood flow.

He reeled, and on Herminius
   He leaned one breathing-space;
Then, like a wild-cat mad with wounds,
   Sprang right at Astur's face:
Through teeth and skull and helmet
   So fierce a thrust he sped,
The good sword stood a hand-breadth out
   Behind the Tuscan's head.

And the great Lord of Luna
   Fell at that deadly stroke,
As falls on Mount Alvernus
   A thunder-smitten oak.
Far o'er the crashing forest
   The giant arms lie spread;
And the pale augurs, muttering low,
   Gaze on the blasted head.

On Astur's throat Horatius
   Right firmly pressed his heel,
And thrice and four times tugged amain
   Ere he wrenched out the steel.
" And see," he cried, " the welcome,
   Fair guests, that waits you here!
What noble Lucumo comes next
   To taste our Roman cheer? "

But at his haughty challenge
   A sullen murmur ran,
Mingled of wrath and shame and dread,
   Along that glittering van.
There lacked not men of prowess,
Nor men of lordly race;
For all Etruria's noblest
   Were round the fatal place.

But all Etruria's noblest
   Felt their hearts sink to see
On the earth the bloody corpses,
   In the path the dauntless Three:
And, from the ghastly entrance
   Where those bold Romans stood,
All shrank, like boys who, unaware,
Ranging the woods to start a hare,
Come to the mouth of the dark lair
Where, growling low, a fierce old bear
   Lies amidst bones and blood.

Was none who would be foremost
   To lead such dire attack:
But those behind cried " Forward! "
   And those before cried " Back! "
And backward now and forward
   Wavers the deep array;
And on the tossing sea of steel
   To and fro the standards reel;
And the victorious trumpet-peal
   Dies fitfully away.

But meanwhile axe and lever
   Have manfully been plied;
And now the bridge hangs tottering
   Above the boiling tide.
" Come back, come back, Horatius! '
   Loud cried the Fathers all.
" Back, Lartius! back, Herminius!
   Back, ere the ruin fall! "

Back darted Spurius Lartius;
   Herminius darted back:
And, as they passed, beneath their feet
   They felt the timbers crack.

But when they turned their faces,
   And on the farther shore
Saw brave Horatius stand alone,
   They would have crossed once more.

But with a crash like thunder
   Fell every loosened beam,
And, like a dam, the mighty wreck
   Lay right athwart the stream.
And a long shout of triumph
   Rose from the walls of Rome,
As to the highest turret-tops
   Was splash'd the yellow foam.

And, like a horse unbroken
   When first he feels the rein,
The furious river struggled hard,
   And tossed his tawny mane,
And burst the curb, and bounded,
   Rejoicing to be free,
And whirling down, in fierce career,
Battlement and plank and pier,
   Rushed headlong to the sea.

Alone stood brave Horatius,
   But constant still in mind;
Thrice thirty thousand foes before,
   And the broad flood behind,
" Down with him! " cried false Sextus,
   With a smile on his pale face.
" Now yield thee," cried Lars Porsena,
   " Now yield thee to our grace."

Round turned he, as not deigning
   Those craven ranks to see;

Naught spake he to Lars Porsena,
　To Sextus naught spake he;
But he saw on Palatinus
　The white porch of his home;
And he spake to the noble river
　That rolls by the towers of Rome.

" Oh, Tiber! father Tiber!
　To whom the Romans pray,
A Roman's life, a Roman's arms,
　Take thou in charge this day! "
So he spake, and speaking sheathed
　The good sword by his side,
And with his harness on his back
　Plunged headlong in the tide.

No sound of joy or sorrow
　Was heard from either bank;
But friends and foes in dumb surprise,
With parted lips and straining eyes,
　Stood gazing where he sank;
And when above the surges
　They saw his crest appear,
All Rome sent forth a rapturous cry,
And even the ranks of Tuscany
　Could scarce forbear to cheer.

But fiercely ran the current,
　Swollen high by months of rain:
And fast his blood was flowing,
　And he was sore in pain,
And heavy with his armour,
　And spent with changing blows;
And oft they thought him sinking,
　But still again he rose.

Never, I ween, did swimmer,
   In such an evil case,
Struggle through such a raging flood
   Safe to the landing place:
But his limbs were borne up bravely
   By the brave heart within,
And our good father Tiber
   Bore bravely up his chin.

And now he feels the bottom;
   Now on dry earth he stands;
Now round him throng the Fathers
   To press his gory hands;
And now, with shouts and clapping,
   And noise of weeping loud,
He enters through the River-Gate,
   Borne by the joyous crowd.

They gave him of the corn-land,
   That was of public right,
As much as two strong oxen
   Could plough from morn till night;
And they made a molten image,
   And set it up on high,
And there it stands unto this day
   To witness if I lie.

It stands in the Comitium,
   Plain for all folk to see;
Horatius in his harness,
   Halting upon one knee:
And underneath is written,
   In letters all of gold,
How valiantly he kept the bridge
   In the brave days of old.

And still his name sounds stirring
   Unto the men of Rome,
As the trumpet-blast that cries to them
   To charge the Volscian home;
And wives still pray to Juno
   For boys with hearts as bold
As his who kept the bridge so well
   In the brave days of old.

And in the nights of winter,
   When the cold north winds blow,
And the long howling of the wolves
   Is heard amidst the snow;
When round the lonely cottage
   Roars loud the tempest's din,
And the good logs of Algidus
   Roar louder yet within;

When the oldest cask is opened,
   And the largest lamp is lit;
When the chestnuts glow in the embers,
   And the kid turns on the spit;
When young and old in circle
   Around the firebrands close;
When the girls are weaving baskets,
   And the lads are shaping bows;

When the goodman mends his armour
   And trims his helmet's plume;
When the goodwife's shuttle merrily
   Goes flashing through the loom;
With weeping and with laughter
   Still is the story told,
How well Horatius kept the bridge
   In the brave days of old.

M.V.

The Armada

LORD MACAULAY

ATTEND, all ye who list to hear our noble England's
    praise;
I tell of the thrice-famous deeds she wrought in ancient
    days,
When that great fleet invincible against her bore in vain
The richest spoils of Mexico, the stoutest hearts of Spain.
It was about the lovely close of a warm summer day,
There came a gallant merchant-ship full sail to Plymouth
    Bay;
Her crew had seen Castile's black fleet, beyond Aurigny's
    isle,
At earliest twilight, on the waves lie heaving many a mile.
At sunrise she escaped their van, by God's especial grace;
And the tall Pinta till the noon had held her close in
    chase.
Forthwith a guard at every gun was placed along the wall;
The beacon blazed upon the roof of Edgcumbe's lofty hall;
Many a light fishing bark put out to pry along the coast,
And with loose rein and bloody spur rode inland many a
    post.
With his white hair unbonneted, the stout old sheriff
    comes;
Behind him march the halberdiers; before him sound the
    drums;
His yeomen round the market cross make clear an ample
    space;
For there behoves him to set up the standard of Her Grace.
And haughtily the trumpets peal, and gaily dance the
    bells,
As slow upon the labouring wind the royal blazon swells.

Look how the Lion of the sea lifts up his ancient crown,
And underneath his deadly paw treads the gay lilies
    down.
So stalked he when he turned to flight, on that famed
    Picard field,
Bohemia's plume, and Genoa's bow, and Cæsar's eagle
    shield.
So glared he when at Agincourt in wrath he turned to
    bay,
And crushed and torn beneath his claws the princely
    hunters lay.
Ho, strike the flagstaff deep, Sir Knight!   Ho, scatter
    flowers, fair maids!
Ho, gunners, fire a loud salute!   Ho, gallants, draw your
    blades!
Thou sun, shine on her joyously, ye breezes, waft her wide,
Our glorious SEMPER EADEM, the banner of our pride!
The freshening breeze of eve unfurled that banner's
    massy fold;
The parting gleam of sunshine kissed that haughty scroll
    of gold;
Night sank upon the dusky beach, and on the purple sea,
Such night in England ne'er had been, nor e'er again
    shall be.
From Eddystone to Berwick bounds, from Lynn to Mil-
    ford Bay,
That time of slumber was as bright and busy as the day;
For swift to east and swift to west the ghastly war-flame
    spread,
High on St. Michael's Mount it shone; it shone on
    Beachy Head;
Far on the deep the Spaniard saw, along each southern
    shire,
Cape beyond cape, in endless range, those twinkling
    points of fire.

The fisher left his skiff to rock on Tamar's glittering
    waves,
The rugged miners poured to war from Mendip's sunless
    caves;
O'er Longleat's towers, o'er Cranbourne's oaks, the fiery
    herald flew:
He roused the shepherds of Stonehenge, the rangers of
    Beaulieu.
Right sharp and quick the bells all night rang out from
    Bristol town,
And ere the day three hundred horse had met on Clifton
    down.
The sentinel on Whitehall gate looked forth into the
    night,
And saw o'erhanging Richmond Hill the streak of blood-
    red light;
Then bugle's note and cannon's roar the death-like sil-
    ence broke,
And with one start, and with one cry, the royal city
    woke.
At once on all her stately gates arose the answering fires;
At once the wild alarum clashed from all her reeling
    spires;
From all the batteries of the Tower pealed loud the voice
    of fear;
And all the thousand masts of Thames sent back a louder
    cheer;
And from the farthest wards was heard the rush of hurry-
    ing feet,
And the broad streams of pikes and flags rushed down
    each roaring street.
And broader still became the blaze, and louder still the
    din,
As fast from every village round the horse came spurring
    in.

And eastward straight from wild Blackheath the warlike
errand went,

And roused in many an ancient hall the gallant squires of
Kent.

Southward from Surrey's pleasant hills flew those bright
couriers forth;

High on bleak Hampstead's swarthy moor they started for
the north;

And on, and on, without a pause, untired they bounded
still:

All night from tower to tower they sprang; they sprang
from hill to hill:

Till the proud Peak unfurled the flag o'er Darwin's rocky
dales,

Till like volcanoes flared to heaven the stormy hills of
Wales,

Till twelve fair counties saw the blaze on Malvern's lonely
height,

Till streamed in crimson on the wind the Wrekin's crest
of light,

Till broad and fierce the star came forth on Ely's stately
fane,

And tower and hamlet rose in arms o'er all the boundless
plain;

Till Belvoir's lordly terraces the sign to Lincoln sent,

And Lincoln sped the message on o'er the wide vale of
Trent;

Till Skiddaw saw the fire that burned on Gaunt's em-
battled pile,

And the red glare on Skiddaw roused the burghers of
Carlisle. . . .

The Burial of Sir John Moore

CHARLES WOLFE

Not a drum was heard, not a funeral note,
  As his corse to the rampart we hurried;
Not a soldier discharged his farewell shot
  O'er the grave where our hero we buried.

We buried him darkly at dead of night,
  The sods with our bayonets turning,
By the struggling moonbeam's misty light,
  And the lantern dimly burning.

No useless coffin enclosed his breast,
  Not in sheet nor in shroud we wound him;
But he lay like a warrior taking his rest,
  With his martial cloak around him.

Few and short were the prayers we said,
  And we spoke not a word of sorrow;
But we steadfastly gazed on the face that was dead,
  And we bitterly thought of the morrow.

We thought, as we hollowed his narrow bed,
  And smoothed down his lonely pillow,
How the foe and the stranger would tread o'er his head,
  And we far away on the billow!

Lightly they'll talk of the spirit that's gone,
  And o'er his cold ashes upbraid him,—
But little he'll reck, if they let him sleep on
  In the grave where a Briton has laid him.

But half of our heavy task was done
    When the clock struck the hour for retiring;
And we heard the distant and random gun
    That the foe was sullenly firing.

Slowly and sadly we laid him down,
    From the field of his fame fresh and gory;
We carved not a line, and we raised not a stone,
    But we left him alone with his glory.

The Burial of Moses

MRS. C. F. ALEXANDER

By Nebo's lonely mountain,
    On this side Jordan's wave,
In a vale in the land of Moab
    There lies a lonely grave.
And no man knows that sepulchre,
    And no man saw it e'er,
For the angels of God upturned the sod,
    And laid the dead man there.

That was the grandest funeral
    That ever pass'd on earth;
But no man heard the trampling,
    Or saw the train go forth—
Noiselessly as the daylight
    Comes back when night is done,
And the crimson streak on ocean's cheek
    Grows into the great sun.

Noiselessly as the springtime
  Her crown of verdure weaves,
And all the trees on all the hills
  Open their thousand leaves;
So without sound of music,
  Or voice of them that wept,
Silently down from the mountain's crown,
  The great procession swept.

Perchance the bald old eagle,
  On grey Beth-Peor's height,
Out of his lonely eyrie,
  Looked on the wondrous sight;
Perchance the lion stalking
  Still shuns that hallow'd spot,
For beast and bird have seen and heard
  That which man knoweth not.

But when the warrior dieth,
  His comrades in the war,
With arms reversed and muffled drum,
  Follow his funeral car;
They show the banners taken,
  They tell his battles won,
And after him lead his masterless steed,
  While peals the minute-gun.

Amid the noblest of the land,
  We lay the sage to rest,
And give the bard an honour'd place
  With costly marble drest,
In the great minster transept,
  Where lights like glories fall,
And the organ rings, and the sweet choir sings
  Along the emblazon'd wall.

This was the truest warrior,
   That ever buckled sword,
This the most gifted poet
   That ever breath'd a word;
And never earth's philosopher
   Traced with his golden pen,
On the deathless page, truths half so sage
   As he wrote down for men.

And had he not high honour,—
   The hill-side for a pall,
To lie in state, while angels wait
   With stars for tapers tall,
And the dark rock-pines, like tossing plumes,
   Over his bier to wave,
And God's own hand in that lonely land
   To lay him in the grave?

In that strange grave without a name,
   Whence his uncoffin'd clay
Shall break again, O wondrous thought!
   Before the Judgment day,
And stand with glory wrapt around,
   On the hills he never trod,
And speak of the strife, that won our life
   With the Incarnate Son of God.

O lonely grave in Moab's land!
   O dark Beth-Peor's hill!
Speak to these curious hearts of ours,
   And teach them to be still.
God hath his mysteries of grace,
   Ways that we cannot tell;
He hides them deep, like the hidden sleep
   Of him He loved so well.

I remember, I remember

THOMAS HOOD

I REMEMBER, I remember
The house where I was born,
The little window where the sun
Came peeping in at morn;
He never came a wink too soon
Nor brought too long a day;
But now, I often wish the night
Had borne my breath away.

I remember, I remember
The roses, red and white,
The violets, and the lily-cups—
Those flowers made of light!
The lilacs where the robin built,
And where my brother set
The laburnum on his birthday,—
The tree is living yet!

I remember, I remember
Where I was used to swing,
And thought the air must rush as fresh
To swallows on the wing;
My spirit flew in feathers then
That is so heavy now,
The summer pools could hardly cool
The fever on my brow.

I remember, I remember
The fir-trees dark and high;
I used to think their slender tops
Were close against the sky:
It was a childish ignorance,
But now 'tis little joy
To know I'm farther off from Heaven
Than when I was a boy.

The Walrus and the Carpenter

LEWIS CARROLL

THE sun was shining on the sea,
    Shining with all his might:
He did his very best to make
    The billows smooth and bright—
And this was odd, because it was
    The middle of the night.

The moon was shining sulkily,
    Because she thought the sun
Had got no business to be there
    After the day was done—
" It's very rude of him," she said,
    " To come and spoil the fun."

The sea was wet as wet could be,
    The sands were dry as dry.
You could not see a cloud, because
    No cloud was in the sky:
No birds were flying overhead—
    There were no birds to fly.

The Walrus and the Carpenter
   Were walking close at hand;
They wept like anything to see
   Such quantities of sand;
" If this were only cleared away,"
   They said, " it *would* be grand."

" If seven maids with seven mops
   Swept it for half a year,
Do you suppose," the Walrus said,
   " That they could get it clear? "
" I doubt it," said the Carpenter,
   And shed a bitter tear.

" O Oysters, come and walk with us! "
   The Walrus did beseech.
" A pleasant walk, a pleasant talk,
   Along the briny beach:
We cannot do with more than four,
   To give a hand to each."

The eldest Oyster looked at him,
   But never a word he said:
The eldest Oyster winked his eye,
   And shook his heavy head—
Meaning to say he did not choose
   To leave the oyster bed.

But four young Oysters hurried up,
   All eager for the treat:
Their coats were brushed, their faces washed,
   Their shoes were clean and neat—
And this was odd, because, you know,
   They hadn't any feet.

Four other Oysters followed them,
    And yet another four;
And thick and fast they came at last,
    And more, and more, and more—
All hopping through the frothy waves,
    And scrambling to the shore.

The Walrus and the Carpenter
    Walked on a mile or so,
And then they rested on a rock
    Conveniently low.
And all the little Oysters stood
    And waited in a row.

" The time has come," the Walrus said,
    " To talk of many things:
Of shoes—and ships—and sealing-wax—
    Of cabbages—and kings—
And why the sea is boiling hot—
    And whether pigs have wings."

" But wait a bit," the Oysters cried,
    " Before we have our chat;
For some of us are out of breath,
    And all of us are fat! "
" No hurry! " said the Carpenter.
    They thanked him much for that.

" A loaf of bread," the Walrus said,
    " Is what we chiefly need:
Pepper and vinegar, besides,
    Are very good indeed—
Now, if you're ready, Oysters dear,
    We can begin to feed."

" But not on us! " the Oysters cried,
  Turning a little blue.
" After such kindness, that would be
  A dismal thing to do! "
" The night is fine," the Walrus said,
  " Do you admire the view? "

" It was so kind of you to come!
  And you are very nice! "
The Carpenter said nothing but
  " Cut us another slice:
I wish you were not quite so deaf—
  I've had to ask you twice."

" It seems a shame," the Walrus said
  " To play them such a trick,
After we've brought them out so far,
  And made them trot so quick! "
The Carpenter said nothing but
  " The butter's spread too thick."

" I weep for you," the Walrus said:
  " I deeply sympathize."
With sobs and tears he sorted out
  Those of the largest size,
Holding his pocket-handkerchief
  Before his streaming eyes.

" O Oysters," said the Carpenter,
  " You've had a pleasant run!
Shall we be trotting home again? "
  But answer came there none—
And this was scarcely odd, because
  They'd eaten every one.

The Lobster Quadrille

LEWIS CARROLL

" WILL you walk a little faster? " said a whiting to a snail
" There's a porpoise close behind us, and he's treading on
    my tail.
See how eagerly the lobsters and the turtles all advance!
They are waiting on the shingle—will you come and join
    the dance?
    Will you, won't you, will you, won't you, will you join
      the dance?
    Will you, won't you, will you, won't you, won't you join
      the dance?

" You can really have no notion how delightful it will be,
When they take us up and throw us, with the lobsters, out
    to sea! "
But the snail replied " Too far, too far! " and gave a look
    askance—
Said he thanked the whiting kindly, but he would not
    join the dance.
    Would not, could not, would not, could not, would not
    join the dance.
    Would not, could not, would not, could not, could not
    join the dance.

" What matters it how far we go? " his scaly friend replied.
" There is another shore, you know, upon the other side.
The further off from England the nearer is to France—
Then turn not pale, beloved snail, but come and join the
    dance.
    Will you, won't you, will you, won't you, will you join
      the dance?
    Will you, won't you, will you, won't you, won't you
    join the dance? "

Father William

LEWIS CARROLL

" You are old, Father William," the young man said,
     " And your hair has become very white;
And yet you incessantly stand on your head—
     Do you think, at your age, it is right? "

" In my youth," Father William replied to his son,
     " I feared it might injure the brain;
But, now that I'm perfectly sure I have none,
     Why, I do it again and again."

" You are old," said the youth, " as I mentioned before,
     And have grown most uncommonly fat;
Yet you turned a back-somersault in at the door—
     Pray, what is the reason of that? "

" In my youth," said the sage, as he shook his grey locks,
     " I kept all my limbs very supple
By the use of this ointment—one shilling the box—
     Allow me to sell you a couple? "

" You are old," said the youth, " and your jaws are too
     weak
     For anything tougher than suet;
Yet you finished the goose, with the bones and the beak—
     Pray, how did you manage to do it? "

" In my youth," said his father, " I took to the law,
     And argued each case with my wife;
And the muscular strength, which it gave to my jaw,
     Has lasted the rest of my life."

" You are old," said the youth, " one would hardly
    suppose
That your eye was as steady as ever;
Yet you balance an eel on the end of your nose—
    What made you so awfully clever? "

" I have answered three questions, and that is enough,"
    Said his father; " don't give yourself airs!
Do you think I can listen all day to such stuff?
    Be off, or I'll kick you down stairs! "

Piping down the Valleys Wild

WILLIAM BLAKE

PIPING down the valleys wild,
    Piping songs of pleasant glee,
On a cloud I saw a child,
    And, he, laughing, said to me:

" Pipe a song about a lamb,"
    So I piped with merry cheer;
" Piper, pipe that song again."
    So I piped, he wept to hear.

" Drop thy pipe, thy happy pipe,
    Sing thy songs of happy cheer."
So I sang the same again,
    While he wept with joy to hear.

" Piper, sit thee down and write
    In a book that all may read."
So he vanish'd from my sight;
    And I pluck'd a hollow reed,

M.V.

And I made a rural pen,
   And I stain'd the water clear,
And I wrote my happy songs
   Every child may joy to hear.

Hohenlinden

THOMAS CAMPBELL

On Linden, when the sun was low,
All bloodless lay th' untrodden snow,
And dark as winter was the flow
Of Iser, rolling rapidly:

But Linden saw another sight,
When the drum beat at dead of night,
Commanding fires of death to light
The darkness of her scenery.

By torch and trumpet fast array'd,
Each horseman drew his battle-blade,
And furious every charger neigh'd
To join the dreadful revelry.

Then shook the hills with thunder riven,
Then rush'd the steed to battle driven,
And louder than the bolts of heaven,
Far flash'd the red artillery.

But redder yet that light shall glow
On Linden's hills of stainéd snow,
And bloodier yet the torrent flow
Of Iser, rolling rapidly.

'Tis morn, but scarce yon level sun
Can pierce the war-clouds, rolling dun,
Where furious Frank, and fiery Hun,
Shout in their sulph'rous canopy.

The combat deepens.   On, ye brave,
Who rush to glory, or the grave!
Wave, Munich! all thy banners wave,
And charge with all thy chivalry!

Few, few, shall part where many meet!
The snow shall be their winding-sheet,
And every turf beneath their feet
Shall be a soldier's sepulchre.

Ye Mariners of England

THOMAS CAMPBELL

Ye Mariners of England!
That guard our native seas;
Whose flag has braved, a thousand years,
The battle and the breeze!
Your glorious standard launch again
To match another foe!
And sweep through the deep,
While the stormy tempests blow;
While the battle rages loud and long,
And the stormy tempests blow.

The spirits of your fathers
Shall start from every wave!—
For the deck it was their field of fame,
And Ocean was their grave:

Where Blake and mighty Nelson fell,
Your manly hearts shall glow,
As ye sweep through the deep,
While the stormy tempests blow;
While the battle rages loud and long,
And the stormy tempests blow.

Britannia needs no bulwark,
No towers along the steep;
Her march is o'er the mountain-waves,
Her home is on the deep.
With thunders from her native oak,
She quells the floods below,—
As they roar on the shore,
When the stormy tempests blow;
When the battle rages loud and long,
And the stormy tempests blow.

The meteor flag of England
Shall yet terrific burn;
Till danger's troubled night depart,
And the star of peace return.
Then, then, ye ocean-warriors!
Our song and feast shall flow
To the fame of your name,
When the storm has ceased to blow;
When the fiery fight is heard no more,
And the storm has ceased to blow.

The Bells of Heaven

RALPH HODGSON

'Twould ring the bells of heaven
The wildest peal for years,
If Parson lost his senses
And people came to theirs,
And he and they together
Knelt down with angry prayers
For tamed and shabby tigers
And dancing dogs and bears,
And wretched blind pit-ponies,
And little hunted hares.

There was an Indian

SIR JOHN SQUIRE

There was an Indian, who had known no change,
Who strayed content along a sunlit beach
Gathering shells.   He heard a sudden strange
Commingled noise; looked up; and gasped for speech.
For in the bay, where nothing was before,
Moved on the sea, by magic, huge canoes,
With bellying cloths on poles, and not one oar,
And fluttering coloured signs and clambering crews.
And he, in fear, this naked man alone,
His fallen hands forgetting all their shells,
His lips gone pale, knelt low behind a stone,
And stared, and saw, and did not understand,
Columbus's doom-burdened caravels
Slant to the shore, and all their seamen land.

Ode to the North-east Wind

CHARLES KINGSLEY

WELCOME, wild North-easter!
   Shame it is to see
Odes to every zephyr;
   Ne'er a verse to thee.
Welcome, black North-easter!
   O'er the German foam;
O'er the Danish moorlands,
   From thy frozen home.
Tired we are of summer,
   Tired of gaudy glare,
Showers soft and steaming,
   Hot and breathless air.
Tired of listless dreaming,
   Through the lazy day:
Jovial wind of winter,
   Turn us out to play.
Sweep the golden reed-beds;
   Crisp the lazy dyke;
Hunger into madness
   Every plunging pike.
Fill the lake with wild-fowl;
   Fill the marsh with snipe;
While on dreary moorlands
   Lonely curlew pipe.
Through the black fir-forest
   Thunder harsh and dry,
Shattering down the snow-flakes
   Off the curdled sky.
Hark! the brave North-easter!
   Breast-high lies the scent,

On by bolt and headland,
  Over heath and bent.
Chime, ye dappled darlings,
  Through the sleet and snow.
Who can over-ride you?
  Let the horses go!
Chime, ye dappled darlings,
  Down the roaring blast;
You shall see a fox die
  Ere an hour be past.
Go! and rest to-morrow,
  Hunting in your dreams,
While our skates are ringing
  O'er the frozen streams.
Let the luscious South-wind
  Breathe in lovers' sighs,
While the lazy gallants
  Bask in ladies' eyes.
What does he but soften
  Heart alike and pen?
'Tis the hard grey weather
  Breeds hard English men.
What's the soft South-wester?
  'Tis the ladies' breeze,
Bringing home their true loves
  Out of all the seas:
But the black North-easter,
  Through the snowstorm hurled,
Drives our English hearts of oak
  Seaward round the world.
Come, as came our fathers,
  Heralded by thee,
Conquering from the eastward,
  Lords by land and sea.

Come; and strong within us
   Stir the Vikings' blood;
Bracing brain and sinew;
   Blow, thou wind of God!

The Song of the Bow

SIR ARTHUR CONAN DOYLE

WHAT of the bow?
   The bow was made in England:
Of true wood, of yew-wood,
   The wood of English bows;
     So men who are free
     Love the old yew-tree
And the land where the yew-tree grows.

What of the cord?
   The cord was made in England:
A rough cord, a tough cord,
   A cord that bowmen love;
     And so we will sing
     Of the hempen string
And the land where the cord was wove.

What of the shaft?
   The shaft was cut in England:
A long shaft, a strong shaft,
   Barbed and trim and true;
     So we'll drink all together
     To the grey goose-feather
And the land where the grey goose flew.

What of the mark?
  Ah, seek it not in England,
A bold mark, our old mark
  Is waiting over-sea.
    When the strings harp in chorus,
    And the lion flag is o'er us,
It is there that our mark will be.

What of the men?
  The men were bred in England:
The bowmen—the yeomen,
  The lads of dale and fell.
    Here's to you—and to you!
    To the hearts that are true
And the land where the true hearts dwell.

The Loss of the Birkenhead

SIR F. H. DOYLE

RIGHT on our flank the crimson sun went down,
  The deep sea rolled around in dark repose,
When, like the wild shriek from some captured town,
  A cry of women rose.

The stout ship Birkenhead lay hard and fast,
  Caught, without hope, upon a hidden rock;
Her timbers thrilled as nerves, when thro' them passed
  The spirit of that shock.

And ever like base cowards, who leave their ranks
  In danger's hour before the rush of steel,
Drifted away, disorderly, the planks,
  From underneath her keel.

D*

Confusion spread, for, though the coast seemed near,
  Sharks hovered thick along that white sea-brink.
The boats could hold?—not all—and it was clear
  She was about to sink.

" Out with those boats, and let us haste away ",
  Cried one, " ere yet yon sea the bark devours."
The man thus clamouring was, I scarce need say,
  No officer of ours.

We knew our duty better than to care
  For such loose babblers, and made no reply,
Till our good colonel gave the word, and there
  Formed us in line to die.

There rose no murmur from the ranks, no thought,
  By shameful strength, unhonoured life to seek;
Our post to quit we were not trained, nor taught
  To trample down the weak.

So we made women with their children go,
  The oars ply back agen, and yet agen!
Whilst, inch by inch, the drowning ship sank low,
  Still under steadfast men.

What follows why recall?   The brave who died,
  Died without flinching in the bloody surf;
They sleep as well, beneath that purple tide,
  As others, under turf.

They sleep as well, and, roused from their wild grave,
  Wearing their wounds like stars, shall rise again,
Joint-heirs with Christ, because they bled to save
  His weak ones, not in vain.

Good King Wenceslas

J. M. NEALE

GOOD King Wenceslas looked out
  On the Feast of Stephen,
When the snow lay round about,
  Deep, and crisp, and even.

Brightly shone the moon that night,
  Though the frost was cruel,
When a poor man came in sight,
  Gath'ring winter fuel.

" Hither, page, and stand by me,
  If thou know'st it, telling,
Yonder peasant, who is he?
  Where and what his dwelling? "

" Sire, he lives a good league hence,
  Underneath the mountain;
Right against the forest fence,
  By Saint Agnes' fountain."

" Bring me flesh and bring me wine,
  Bring me pine-logs hither;
Thou and I will see him dine,
  When we bear them thither."

Page and monarch, forth they went,
  Forth they went together;
Through the rude wind's wild lament
  And the bitter weather.

" Sire, the night is darker now,
   And the wind blows stronger;
Fails my heart, I know not how,
   I can go no longer."

" Mark my footsteps, good my page;
   Tread thou in them boldly:
Thou shalt find the winter's rage
   Freeze thy blood less coldly."

In his master's steps he trod,
   Where the snow lay dinted;
Heat was in the very sod
   Which the saint had printed.

Therefore, Christian men, be sure,
   Wealth or rank possessing,
Ye who now will bless the poor,
   Shall yourselves find blessing.

PART II

Vitaï Lampada

SIR HENRY NEWBOLT

THERE's a breathless hush in the Close to-night—
   Ten to make and the match to win—
A bumping pitch and a blinding light,
   An hour to play and the last man in.
And it's not for the sake of a ribboned coat,
   Or the selfish hope of a season's fame,
But his Captain's hand on his shoulder smote—
   " Play up! play up! and play the game! "

The sand of the desert is sodden red,—
   Red with the wreck of a square that broke;—
The Gatling's jammed and the Colonel dead,
   And the regiment blind with dust and smoke.
The river of death has brimmed his banks,
   And England's far, and Honour a name,
But the voice of a schoolboy rallies the ranks:
   " Play up! play up! and play the game! "

This is the word that year by year,
   While in her place the School is set,
Every one of her sons must hear,
   And none that hears it dare forget.
This they all with a joyful mind
   Bear through life like a torch in flame,
And falling fling to the host behind—
   " Play up! play up! and play the game! "

Drake's Drum

SIR HENRY NEWBOLT

DRAKE he's in his hammock an' a thousand mile away,
  (Capten, art tha sleepin' there below?)
Slung atween the round shot in Nombre Dios Bay,
  An' dreamin' arl the time o' Plymouth Hoe.
Yarnder lumes the Island, yarnder lie the ships,
  Wi' sailor-lads a-dancin' heel-an'-toe,
An' the shore-lights flashin', an' the night-tide dashin',
  He sees et arl so plainly as he saw et long ago.

Drake he was a Devon man, an' rüled the Devon seas,
  (Capten, art tha sleepin' there below?)
Rovin' tho' his death fell, he went wi' heart at ease,
  An' dreamin' arl the time o' Plymouth Hoe.
" Take my drum to England, hang et by the shore,
  Strike et when your powder's runnin' low;
If the Dons sight Devon, I'll quit the port o' Heaven,
  An' drum them up the Channel as we drummed them
    long ago."

Drake he's in his hammock till the great Armadas come,
  (Capten, art tha sleepin' there below?)
Slung atween the round shot, listenin' for the drum,
  An' dreamin' arl the time o' Plymouth Hoe.
Call him on the deep sea, call him up the Sound,
  Call him when ye sail to meet the foe;
Where the old trade's plyin' an' the old flag flyin'
  They shall find him ware an' wakin', as they found him
    long ago!

Admirals All

SIR HENRY NEWBOLT

EFFINGHAM, Grenville, Raleigh, Drake,
    Here's to the bold and free!
Benbow, Collingwood, Byron, Blake,
    Hail to the Kings of the Sea!
Admirals all, for England's sake,
    Honour be yours and fame!
And honour, as long as waves shall break,
    To Nelson's peerless name!

> *Admirals all, for England's sake,*
> *   Honour be yours and fame!*
> *And honour, as long as waves shall break,*
> *   To Nelson's peerless name!*

Essex was fretting in Cadiz Bay
    With the galleons fair in sight;
Howard at last must give him his way,
    And the word was passed to fight.
Never was schoolboy gayer than he,
    Since holidays first began:
He tossed his bonnet to wind and sea,
    And under the guns he ran.

Drake nor devil nor Spaniard feared,
    Their cities he put to the sack;
He singed His Catholic Majesty's beard,
    And harried his ships to wrack.
He was playing at Plymouth a rubber of bowls
    When the great Armada came;
But he said, " They must wait their turn, good souls,"
    And he stooped, and finished the game.

Fifteen sail were the Dutchmen bold,
    Duncan he had but two:
But he anchored them fast where the Texel shoaled,
    And his colours aloft he flew.
" I've taken the depth to a fathom," he cried,
    " And I'll sink with a right good will,
For I know when we're all of us under the tide,
    My flag will be fluttering still."

Splinters were flying above, below,
    When Nelson sailed the Sound:
" Mark you, I wouldn't be elsewhere now,"
    Said he, " for a thousand pound! "
The Admiral's signal bade him fly,
    But he wickedly wagged his head,
He clapped the glass to his sightless eye,
    And " I'm damned if I see it! " he said.

Admirals all, they said their say
    (The echoes are ringing still),
Admirals all, they went their way
    To the haven under the hill.
But they left us a kingdom none can take,
    The realm of the circling sea,
To be ruled by the rightful sons of Blake
    And the Rodneys yet to be.

    Admirals all, for England's sake,
        Honour be yours and fame!
    And honour, as long as waves shall break,
        To Nelson's peerless name!

If—

RUDYARD KIPLING

IF you can keep your head when all about you
   Are losing theirs and blaming it on you;
If you can trust yourself when all men doubt you,
   But make allowance for their doubting too;
If you can wait and not be tired by waiting,
   Or being lied about, don't deal in lies,
Or being hated, don't give way to hating,
   And yet don't look too good, nor talk too wise;

If you can dream—and not make dreams your master;
   If you can think—and not make thoughts your aim;
If you can meet with Triumph and Disaster
   And treat those two impostors just the same;
If you can bear to hear the truth you've spoken
   Twisted by knaves to make a trap for fools,
Or watch the things you gave your life to broken,
   And stoop and build 'em up with worn-out tools;

If you can make one heap of all your winnings
   And risk it on one turn of pitch-and-toss,
And lose, and start again at your beginnings,
   And never breathe a word about your loss;
If you can force your heart and nerve and sinew
   To serve your turn long after they are gone,
And so hold on when there is nothing in you
   Except the Will which says to them: " Hold on! "

If you can talk with crowds and keep your virtue,
   Or walk with Kings—nor lose the common touch;
If neither foes nor loving friends can hurt you;
   If all men count with you, but none too much;

If you can fill the unforgiving minute
　　With sixty seconds' worth of distance run,
Yours is the Earth and everything that's in it,
　　And—which is more—you'll be a Man, my son!

Westminster Bridge

WILLIAM WORDSWORTH

EARTH has not anything to show more fair:
Dull would he be of soul who could pass by
A sight so touching in its majesty:
This City now doth, like a garment, wear
The beauty of the morning; silent, bare,
Ships, towers, domes, theatres, and temples lie
Open unto the fields, and to the sky;
All bright and glittering in the smokeless air.
Never did sun more beautifully steep
In his first splendour, valley, rock, or hill;
Ne'er saw I, never felt, a calm so deep!
The river glideth at his own sweet will:
Dear God! the very houses seem asleep;
And all that mighty heart is lying still!

The British Heritage

WILLIAM WORDSWORTH

IT is not to be thought of that the Flood
Of British freedom, which, to the open sea
Of the world's praise, from dark antiquity
Hath flowed, " with pomp of waters, unwithstood,"
Roused though it be full often to a mood
Which spurns the check of salutary bands,

That this most famous Stream in bogs and sands
Should perish; and to evil and to good
Be lost for ever.   In our halls is hung
Armoury of the invincible Knights of old:
We must be free or die, who speak the tongue
That Shakespeare spake; the faith and morals hold
Which Milton held.—In everything we are sprung
Of Earth's first blood, have titles manifold.

To the Cuckoo

WILLIAM WORDSWORTH

O BLITHE New-comer! I have heard,
I hear thee and rejoice.
O Cuckoo! shall I call thee Bird,
Or but a wandering Voice?

While I am lying on the grass
Thy twofold shout I hear,
From hill to hill it seems to pass,
At once far off, and near.

Though babbling only to the Vale,
Of sunshine and of flowers,
Thou bringest unto me a tale
Of visionary hours.

Thrice welcome, darling of the Spring!
Even yet thou art to me
No bird, but an invisible thing,
A voice, a mystery;

The same whom in my school-boy days
I listened to; that Cry
Which made me look a thousand ways
In bush, and tree, and sky.

To seek thee did I often rove
Through woods and on the green;
And thou wert still a hope, a love;
Still longed for, never seen.

And I can listen to thee yet;
Can lie upon the plain
And listen, till I do beget
That golden time again.

O blessèd Bird! the earth we pace
Again appears to be
An unsubstantial, faery place;
That is fit home for Thee!

June Night

WILLIAM WORDSWORTH

THE sun has long been set,
The stars are out by twos and threes,
The little birds are piping yet
Among the bushes and trees;
There's a cuckoo, and one or two thrushes,
And a far-off wind that rushes,
And a sound of water that gushes,
And the cuckoo's sovereign cry
Fills all the hollow of the sky.

The Daffodils

WILLIAM WORDSWORTH

I WANDERED lonely as a cloud
   That floats on high o'er vales and hills,
When all at once I saw a crowd,
   A host, of golden daffodils,
Beside the lake, beneath the trees,
Fluttering and dancing in the breeze.

Continuous as the stars that shine
   And twinkle on the milky way.
They stretched in never-ending line
   Along the margin of a bay:
Ten thousand saw I at a glance
Tossing their heads in sprightly dance.

The waves beside them danced, but they
   Out-did the sparkling waves in glee:
A Poet could not but be gay
   In such a jocund company!
I gazed—and gazed—but little thought
What wealth the show to me had brought:

For oft, when on my couch I lie
   In vacant or in pensive mood,
They flash upon that inward eye
   Which is the bliss of solitude;
And then my heart with pleasure fills,
And dances with the daffodils.

To Daffodils

ROBERT HERRICK

FAIR Daffodils, we weep to see
  You haste away so soon;
As yet the early-rising sun
  Has not attained its noon.
      Stay, stay,
    Until the hasting day
      Has run
    But to the even-song;
And, having prayed together, we
  Will go with you along.

We have short time to stay, as you,
  We have as short a spring;
As quick a growth to meet decay,
  As you, or anything.
      We die
    As your hours do, and dry
      Away,
    Like to the summer's rain;
Or as the pearls of morning's dew
  Ne'er to be found again.

Elegy written in a Country Churchyard

THOMAS GRAY

THE Curfew tolls the knell of parting day,
The lowing herd wind slowly o'er the lea,
The plowman homeward plods his weary way,
And leaves the world to darkness and to me.

Now fades the glimmering landscape on the sight,
And all the air a solemn stillness holds,
Save where the beetle wheels his droning flight,
And drowsy tinklings lull the distant folds:

Save that from yonder ivy-mantled tow'r
The moping owl does to the moon complain
Of such as, wand'ring near her secret bow'r,
Molest her ancient solitary reign.

Beneath those rugged elms, that yew-tree's shade,
Where heaves the turf in many a mould'ring heap,
Each in his narrow cell for ever laid,
The rude Forefathers of the hamlet sleep.

The breezy call of incense-breathing Morn,
The swallow twitt'ring from the straw-built shed,
The cock's shrill clarion, or the echoing horn,
No more shall rouse them from their lowly bed.

For them no more the blazing hearth shall burn,
Or busy housewife ply her evening care:
No children run to lisp their sire's return,
Or climb his knees the envied kiss to share.

Oft did the harvest to their sickle yield,
Their furrow oft the stubborn glebe has broke;
How jocund did they drive their team afield!
How bowed the woods beneath their sturdy stroke!

Let not Ambition mock their useful toil,
Their homely joys, and destiny obscure;
Nor Grandeur hear with a disdainful smile
The short and simple annals of the poor.

The boast of heraldry, the pomp of pow'r,
And all that beauty, all that wealth e'er gave,
Awaits alike th' inevitable hour:—
The paths of glory lead but to the grave.

Nor you, ye Proud, impute to these the fault,
If Mem'ry o'er their tomb no trophies raise,
Where thro' the long-drawn aisle and fretted vault
The pealing anthem swells the note of praise.

Can storied urn or animated bust
Back to its mansion call the fleeting breath?
Can Honour's voice provoke the silent dust,
Or Flatt'ry soothe the dull cold ear of Death?

Perhaps in this neglected spot is laid
Some heart once pregnant with celestial fire;
Hands, that the rod of empire might have sway'd,
Or wak'd to ecstasy the living lyre.

But Knowledge to their eyes her ample page
Rich with the spoils of time did ne'er unroll;
Chill Penury repressed their noble rage,
And froze the genial current of the soul.

Full many a gem of purest ray serene
The dark unfathomed caves of ocean bear:
Full many a flower is born to blush unseen,
And waste its sweetness on the desert air.

Some village Hampden that with dauntless breast
The little tyrant of his fields withstood;
Some mute inglorious Milton here may rest,
Some Cromwell guiltless of his country's blood.

Th' applause of list'ning senates to command,
The threats of pain and ruin to despise,
To scatter plenty o'er a smiling land,
And read their hist'ry in a nation's eyes,

Their lot forbad: nor circumscribed alone
Their growing virtues, but their crimes confined;
Forbad to wade through slaughter to a throne,
And shut the gates of mercy on mankind,

The struggling pangs of conscious truth to hide,
To quench the blushes of ingenuous shame,
Or heap the shrine of Luxury and Pride
With incense kindled at the Muse's flame.

Far from the madding crowd's ignoble strife,
Their sober wishes never learned to stray;
Along the cool sequestered vale of life
They kept the noiseless tenor of their way.

Yet ev'n these bones from insult to protect
Some frail memorial still erected nigh,
With uncouth rhymes and shapeless sculpture decked,
Implores the passing tribute of a sigh.

Their name, their years, spelt by th' unlettered Muse,
The place of fame and elegy supply:
And many a holy text around she strews,
That teach the rustic moralist to die.

For who, to dumb Forgetfulness a prey,
This pleasing anxious being e'er resign'd,
Left the warm precincts of the cheerful day,
Nor cast one longing ling'ring look behind?

On some fond breast the parting soul relies,
Some pious drops the closing eye requires;
Ev'n from the tomb the voice of Nature cries,
Ev'n in our ashes live their wonted fires.

For thee, who, mindful of th' unhonoured dead,
Dost in these lines their artless tale relate;
If chance, by lonely contemplation led,
Some kindred spirit shall inquire thy fate,

Haply some hoary-headed swain may say,
" Oft have we seen him at the peep of dawn
Brushing with hasty steps the dews away
To meet the sun upon the upland lawn.

" There at the foot of yonder nodding beech
That wreathes its old fantastic roots so high,
His listless length at noontide would he stretch,
And pore upon the brook that babbles by.

" Hard by yon wood, now smiling as in scorn,
Mutt'ring his wayward fancies he would rove,
Now drooping, woeful-wan, like one forlorn,
Or crazed with care, or crossed in hopeless love.

" One morn I missed him on the 'customed hill,
Along the heath and near his fav'rite tree;
Another came; nor yet beside the rill,
Nor up the lawn, nor at the wood was he;

" The next with dirges due in sad array
Slow thro' the church-way path we saw him borne.
Approach and read (for thou canst read) the lay
Graved on the stone beneath yon aged thorn."

THE EPITAPH

Here rests his head upon the lap of Earth
A Youth to Fortune and to Fame unknown.
Fair Science frowned not on his humble birth,
And Melancholy marked him for her own.

Large was his bounty, and his soul sincere,
Heav'n did a recompense as largely send:
He gave to Mis'ry all he had, a tear,
He gained from Heav'n ('twas all he wished) a friend.

No farther seek his merits to disclose,
Or draw his frailties from their dread abode,
(There they alike in trembling hope repose,)
The bosom of his Father and his God.

The Revenge

LORD TENNYSON

At Flores in the Azores Sir Richard Grenville lay,
And a pinnace, like a fluttered bird, came flying from far
    away:
" Spanish ships of war at sea! we have sighted fifty-
    three! "
Then sware Lord Thomas Howard: " 'Fore God I am no
    coward;
But I cannot meet them here, for my ships are out of
    gear,
And the half my men are sick.   I must fly, but follow
    quick.
We are six ships of the line; can we fight with fifty-
    three? "

Then spake Sir Richard Grenville: " I know you are no
    coward;
You fly them for a moment to fight with them again.
But I've ninety men and more that are lying sick ashore.
I should count myself the coward if I left them, my Lord
    Howard,
To these Inquisition dogs and the devildoms of Spain."

So Lord Howard passed away with five ships of war that
    day,
Till he melted like a cloud in the silent summer heaven;
But Sir Richard bore in hand all his sick men from the
    land
Very carefully and slow,
Men of Bideford in Devon,
And we laid them on the ballast down below;

For we brought them all aboard,
And they blest him in their pain, that they were not left
    to Spain,
To the thumbscrew and the stake, for the glory of the
    Lord.

He had only a hundred seamen to work the ship and to
    fight,
And he sailed away from Flores till the Spaniard came in
    sight,
With his huge sea-castles heaving upon the weather bow.
" Shall we fight or shall we fly?
Good Sir Richard, tell us now,
For to fight is but to die!
There'll be little of us left by the time this sun be set."
And Sir Richard said again: " We be all good English
    men.
Let us bang these dogs of Seville, the children of the devil,
For I never turned my back upon Don or devil yet."

Sir Richard spoke, and he laughed, and we roared a
    hurrah, and so
The little Revenge ran on sheer into the heart of the foe,
With her hundred fighters on deck, and her ninety sick
    below;
For half their fleet to the right and half to the left were
    seen,
And the little Revenge ran on through the long sea-lane
    between.

Thousands of their soldiers looked down from their decks
    and laughed,
Thousands of their seamen made mock at the mad little
    craft
Running on and on, till delayed

By their mountain-like San Philip that, of fifteen hundred
    tons,
And up-shadowing high above us with her yawning tiers
    of guns,
Took the breath from her sails, and we stayed.

And while now the great San Philip hung above us like a
    cloud
Whence the thunderbolt will fall
Long and loud,
Four galleons drew away
From the Spanish fleet that day,
And two upon the larboard and two upon the starboard lay,
And the battle thunder broke from them all.

But anon the great San Philip, she bethought herself and
    went,
Having that within her womb that had left her ill
    content;
And the rest they came aboard us, and they fought us
    hand to hand,
For a dozen times they came with their pikes and
    musqueteers,
And a dozen times we shook 'em off as a dog that shakes
    his ears
When he leaps from the water to the land.

And the sun went down, and the stars came out far over
    the summer sea,
But never a moment ceased the fight of the one and the
    fifty-three.
Ship after ship, the whole night long, their high-built
    galleons came,
Ship after ship, the whole night long, with her battle-
    thunder and flame;

Ship after ship, the whole night long, drew back with her
    dead and her shame.
For some were sunk and many were shattered, and so
    could fight us no more—
God of battles, was ever a battle like this in the world
    before?

For he said, " Fight on! fight on! "
Though his vessel was all but a wreck;
And it chanced that, when half of the short summer night
    was gone,
With a grisly wound to be drest he had left the deck,
But a bullet struck him that was dressing it suddenly
    dead,
And himself he was wounded again in the side and the
    head,
And he said, " Fight on! fight on! "

And the night went down and the sun smiled out far over
    the summer sea,
And the Spanish fleet with broken sides lay round us all
    in a ring;
But they dared not touch us again, for they feared that
    we still could sting,
So they watched what the end would be.
And we had not fought them in vain,
But in perilous plight were we,
Seeing forty of our poor hundred were slain,
And half of the rest of us maimed for life
In the crash of the cannonades and the desperate strife;
And the sick men down in the hold were most of them
    stark and cold,
And the pikes were all broken or bent, and the powder
    was all of it spent;
And the masts and the rigging were lying over the side;

E   M.V.

But Sir Richard cried in his English pride:
" We have fought such a fight for a day and a night
As may never be fought again!
We have won great glory, my men!
And a day less or more
At sea or ashore,
We die—does it matter when?
Sink me the ship, Master Gunner—sink her, split her in
    twain!
Fall into the hands of God, not into the hands of
    Spain! "

And the gunner said, " Ay, ay," but the seamen made
    reply:
" We have children, we have wives,
And the Lord hath spared our lives.
We will make the Spaniard promise, if we yield, to let us
    go;
We shall live to fight again and to strike another blow."
And the lion there lay dying, and they yielded to the
    foe.

And the stately Spanish men to their flagship bore him
    then,
Where they laid him by the mast, old Sir Richard caught
    at last,
And they praised him to his face with their courtly foreign
    grace;
But he rose upon their decks, and he cried:
" I have fought for Queen and Faith like a valiant man
    and true;
I have only done my duty as a man is bound to do;
With a joyful spirit I Sir Richard Grenville die! "
And he fell upon their decks and he died.

And they stared at the dead that had been so valiant and
     true,
And had holden the power and glory of Spain so cheap
That he dared her with one little ship and his English
     few;
Was he devil or man?   He was devil for aught they knew,
But they sank his body with honour down into the deep,
And they manned the Revenge with a swarthier alien
     crew,
And away she sailed with her loss and longed for her own;

When a wind from the lands they had ruined awoke from
     sleep,
And the water began to heave and the weather to moan,
And or ever that evening ended a great gale blew,
And a wave like the wave that is raised by an earthquake
     grew,
Till it smote on their hulls and their sails and their masts
     and their flags,
And the whole sea plunged and fell on the shot-shattered
     navy of Spain,
And the little Revenge herself went down by the island
     crags
To be lost evermore in the main.

The Brook

LORD TENNYSON

I COME from haunts of coot and hern,
    I make a sudden sally
And sparkle out among the fern,
    To bicker down a valley.

By thirty hills I hurry down,
    Or slip between the ridges,
By twenty thorps, a little town,
    And half a hundred bridges.

Till last by Philip's farm I flow
    To join the brimming river,
For men may come and men may go,
    But I go on for ever.

I chatter over stony ways,
    In little sharps and trebles,
I bubble into eddying bays,
    I babble on the pebbles.

With many a curve my banks I fret
    By many a field and fallow,
And many a fairy foreland set
    With willow-weed and mallow.

I chatter, chatter, as I flow
    To join the brimming river,
For men may come and men may go,
    But I go on for ever.

I wind about, and in and out,
    With here a blossom sailing,
And here and there a lusty trout,
    And here and there a grayling,

And here and there a foamy flake
    Upon me, as I travel
With many a silvery waterbreak
    Above the golden gravel,

And draw them all along, and flow
   To join the brimming river,
For men may come and men may go,
   But I go on for ever.

I steal by lawns and grassy plots,
   I slide by hazel covers;
I move the sweet forget-me-nots
   That grow for happy lovers.

I slip, I slide, I gloom, I glance,
   Among my skimming swallows;
I make the netted sunbeam dance
   Against my sandy shallows.

I murmur under moon and stars
   In brambly wildernesses;
I linger by my shingly bars;
   I loiter round my cresses:

And out again I curve and flow
   To join the brimming river,
For men may come and men may go,
   But I go on for ever.

Break, break, break

LORD TENNYSON

Break, break, break,
   On thy cold grey stones, O Sea!
And I would that my tongue could utter
   The thoughts that arise in me.

O well for the fisherman's boy,
    That he shouts with his sister at play!
O well for the sailor lad,
    That he sings in his boat on the bay!

And the stately ships go on
    To their haven under the hill;
But O for the touch of a vanish'd hand,
    And the sound of a voice that is still!

Break, break, break,
    At the foot of thy crags, O Sea!
But the tender grace of a day that is dead
    Will never come back to me.

The Splendour falls

LORD TENNYSON

THE splendour falls on castle walls
    And snowy summits old in story;
The long light shakes across the lakes,
    And the wild cataract leaps in glory.
Blow, bugle, blow, set the wild echoes flying,
Blow, bugle; answer, echoes, dying, dying, dying.

O hark, O hear! how thin and clear,
    And thinner, clearer, farther going!
O sweet and far from cliff and scar
    The horns of Elfland faintly blowing!
Blow, let us hear the purple glens replying:
Blow, bugle: answer, echoes, dying, dying, dying.

O love, they die in yon rich sky,
    They faint on hill or field or river:
Our echoes roll from soul to soul,
    And grow for ever and for ever.
Blow, bugle, blow, set the wild echoes flying,
And answer, echoes, answer, dying, dying, dying.

Crossing the Bar

LORD TENNYSON

SUNSET and evening star,
    And one clear call for me!
And may there be no moaning of the bar,
    When I put out to sea,

But such a tide as moving seems asleep,
    Too full for sound and foam,
When that which drew from out the boundless deep
    Turns again home.

Twilight and evening bell,
    And after that the dark!
And may there be no sadness of farewell,
    When I embark;

For tho' from out our bourne of Time and Place
    The flood may bear me far,
I hope to see my Pilot face to face
    When I have crost the bar.

Morte d'Arthur

LORD TENNYSON

So all day long the noise of battle roll'd
Among the mountains by the winter sea;
Until King Arthur's table, man by man,
Had fall'n in Lyonnesse about their Lord,
King Arthur: then, because his wound was deep,
The bold Sir Bedivere uplifted him,
Sir Bedivere, the last of all his knights,
And bore him to a chapel nigh the field,
A broken chancel with a broken cross,
That stood on a dark strait of barren land.
On one side lay the Ocean, and on one
Lay a great water, and the moon was full.
   Then spake King Arthur to Sir Bedivere:
" The sequel of to-day unsolders all
The goodliest fellowship of famous knights
Whereof this world holds record. Such a sleep
They sleep—the men I loved. I think that we
Shall never more, at any future time,
Delight our souls with talk of knightly deeds,
Walking about the gardens and the halls
Of Camelot, as in the days that were.
I perish by this people which I made,—
Tho' Merlin sware that I should come again
To rule once more—but let what will be, be,
I am so deeply smitten thro' the helm
That without help I cannot last till morn.
Thou therefore take my brand Excalibur,
Which was my pride: for thou rememberest how
In those old days, one summer noon, an arm
Rose up from out the bosom of the lake,

Clothed in white samite, mystic, wonderful,
Holding the sword—and how I row'd across
And took it, and have worn it, like a king:
And, wheresoever I am sung or told
In aftertime, this also shall be known:
But now delay not: take Excalibur,
And fling him far into the middle mere:
Watch what thou seëst, and lightly bring me word."

To him replied the bold Sir Bedivere:
" It is not meet, Sir King, to leave thee thus,
Aidless, alone, and smitten thro' the helm.
A little thing may harm a wounded man.
Yet I thy hest will all perform at full,
Watch what I see, and lightly bring thee word."

So saying, from the ruin'd shrine he stept
And in the moon athwart the place of tombs,
Where lay the mighty bones of ancient men,
Old knights, and over them the sea-wind sang
Shrill, chill, with flakes of foam. He, stepping down
By zigzag paths, and juts of pointed rock,
Came on the shining levels of the lake.

There drew he forth the brand Excalibur,
And o'er him, drawing it, the winter moon,
Brightening the skirts of a long cloud, ran forth
And sparkled keen with frost against the hilt:
For all the haft twinkled with diamond sparks,
Myriads of topaz-lights, and jacinth-work
Of subtlest jewellery. He gazed so long
That both his eyes were dazzled, as he stood,
This way and that dividing the swift mind,
In act to throw: but at the last it seem'd
Better to leave Excalibur conceal'd
There in the many-knotted waterflags,
That whistled stiff and dry about the marge.
So strode he back slow to the wounded king.

E*

Then spake King Arthur to Sir Bedivere:
" Hast thou perform'd my mission which I gave?
What is it thou hast seen? or what hast heard? "
　　And answer made the bold Sir Bedivere:
" I heard the ripple washing in the reeds,
And the wild water lapping on the crag."
　　To whom replied King Arthur, faint and pale:
" Thou hast betray'd thy nature and thy name,
Not rendering true answer, as beseem'd
Thy fëalty, nor like a noble knight:
For surer sign had follow'd, either hand,
Or voice, or else a motion of the mere.
This is a shameful thing for men to lie.
Yet now, I charge thee, quickly go again
As thou art lief and dear, and do the thing
I bade thee, watch, and lightly bring me word."
　　Then went Sir Bedivere the second time
Across the ridge, and paced beside the mere,
Counting the dewy pebbles, fix'd in thought;
But when he saw the wonder of the hilt,
How curiously and strangely chased, he smote
His palms together, and he cried aloud:
　　" And if indeed I cast the brand away,
Surely a precious thing, one worthy note,
Should thus be lost for ever from the earth,
Which might have pleased the eyes of many men.
What good should follow this, if this were done?
What harm, undone? deep harm to disobey,
Seeing obedience is the bond of rule.
Were it well to obey then, if a king demand
An act unprofitable, against himself?
The King is sick, and knows not what he does.
What record, or what relic of my lord
Should be to aftertime, but empty breath
And rumours of a doubt? but were this kept,

Stored in some treasure-house of mighty kings,
Some one might show it at a joust of arms,
Saying, ' King Arthur's sword, Excalibur,
Wrought by the lonely maiden of the Lake.
Nine years she wrought it, sitting in the deeps
Upon the hidden bases of the hills.'
So might some old man speak in the aftertime
To all the people, winning reverence.
But now much honour and much fame were lost."

So spake he, clouded with his own conceit,
And hid Excalibur the second time,
And so strode back slow to the wounded King.

Then spoke King Arthur, breathing heavily:
" What is it thou hast seen? or what hast heard? "

And answer made the bold Sir Bedivere:
" I heard the water lapping on the crag,
And the long ripple washing in the reeds."

To whom replied King Arthur, much in wrath:
" Ah, miserable and unkind, untrue,
Unknightly, traitor-hearted! Woe is me!
Authority forgets a dying king,
Laid widow'd of the power in his eye
That bow'd the will. I see thee what thou art,
For thou, the latest-left of all my knights,
In whom should meet the offices of all,
Thou wouldst betray me for the precious hilt;
Either from lust of gold, or like a girl
Valuing the giddy pleasure of the eyes.
Yet, for a man may fail in duty twice,
And the third time may prosper, get thee hence:
But, if thou spare to fling Excalibur,
I will arise and slay thee with my hands."

Then quickly rose Sir Bedivere, and ran,
And, leaping down the ridges lightly, plunged
Among the bulrush-beds, and clutch'd the sword,

And strongly wheel'd and threw it.   The great brand
Made lightnings in the splendour of the moon,
And flashing round and round, and whirl'd in an arch,
Shot like a streamer of the northern morn,
Seen where the moving isles of winter shock
By night, with noises of the northern sea.
So flash'd and fell the brand Excalibur:
But ere he dipt the surface, rose an arm
Clothed in white samite, mystic, wonderful,
And caught him by the hilt, and brandish'd him
Three times, and drew him under in the mere.
And lightly went the other to the King.

   Then spoke King Arthur, drawing thicker breath:
" Now see I by thine eyes that this is done.
Speak out: what is it thou hast heard, or seen? "

   And answer made the bold Sir Bedivere:
" Sir King, I closed mine eyelids, lest the gems
Should blind my purpose, for I never saw,
Nor shall see, here or elsewhere, till I die,
Not tho' I live three lives of mortal men,
So great a miracle as yonder hilt.
Then with both hands I flung him, wheeling him;
But when I look'd again, behold an arm,
Clothed in white samite, mystic, wonderful,
That caught him by the hilt, and brandish'd him
Three times, and drew him under in the mere."

   And answer made King Arthur, breathing hard;
" My end draws nigh! 'tis time that I were gone.
Make broad thy shoulders to receive my weight,
And bear me to the margin! yet I fear
My wound hath taken cold, and I shall die."

   So saying, from the pavement he half rose,
Slowly, with pain, reclining on his arm,
And looking wistfully with wide blue eyes
As in a picture.   Him Sir Bedivere

Remorsefully regarded thro' his tears,
And would have spoken, but he found not words,
Then took with care, and kneeling on one knee,
O'er both his shoulders drew the languid hands,
And rising bore him thro' the place of tombs.

But, as he walk'd, King Arthur panted hard,
Like one that feels a nightmare on his bed
When all the house is mute.   So sigh'd the King,
Muttering and murmuring at his ear, " Quick, quick!
I fear it is too late, and I shall die."
But the other swiftly strode from ridge to ridge,
Clothed with his breath, and looking, as he walk'd,
Larger than human on the frozen hills.
He heard the deep behind him, and a cry
Before.   His own thought drove him, like a goad.
Dry clash'd his harness in the icy caves
And barren chasms, and all to left and right
The bare black cliff clang'd round him, as he based
His feet on juts of slippery crag that rang
Sharp-smitten with the dint of arméd heels—
And on a sudden, lo! the level lake,
And the long glories of the winter moon.

Then saw they how there hove a dusky barge,
Dark as a funeral scarf from stem to stern,
Beneath them! and descending they were ware
That all the decks were dense with stately forms
Black-stoled, black-hooded, like a dream—by these
Three Queens with crowns of gold—and from them rose
A cry that shivered to the tingling stars,
And, as it were one voice, an agony
Of lamentation, like a wind, that shrills
All night in a waste land, where no one comes,
Or hath come, since the making of the world.

Then murmur'd Arthur, " Place me in the barge,"
And to the barge they came.   There those three Queens

Put forth their hands, and took the King, and wept.
But she, that rose the tallest of them all
And fairest, laid his head upon her lap,
And loosed the shatter'd casque, and chafed his hands,
And call'd him by his name, complaining loud,
And dropping bitter tears against his brow
Striped with dark blood: for all his face was white
And colourless, and like the wither'd moon
Smote by the fresh beam of the springing east;
And all his greaves and cuisses dash'd with drops
Of onset! and the light and lustrous curls—
That made his forehead like a rising sun
High from the daïs-throne—were parch'd with dust!
Or, clotted into points and hanging loose,
Mix'd with the knightly growth that fringed his lips.
So like a shatter'd column lay the King;
Not like that Arthur who, with lance in rest,
From spur to plume a star of tournament,
Shot thro' the lists at Camelot, and charged
Before the eyes of ladies and of kings.
    Then loudly cried the bold Sir Bedivere:
" Ah! my Lord Arthur, whither shall I go?
Where shall I hide my forehead and my eyes?
For now I see the true old times are dead,
When every morning brought a noble chance,
And every chance brought out a noble knight.
Such times have been not since the light that led
The holy Elders with the gift of myrrh.
But now the whole ROUND TABLE is dissolved
Which was an image of the mighty world;
And I, the last, go forth companionless,
And the days darken round me, and the years,
Among new men, strange faces, other minds."
    And slowly answer'd Arthur from the barge:
" The old order changeth, yielding place to new,

And God fulfils Himself in many ways,
Lest one good custom should corrupt the world.
Comfort thyself: what comfort is in me?
I have lived my life, and that which I have done
May He within Himself make pure! but thou,
If thou shouldst never see my face again,
Pray for my soul. More things are wrought by prayer
Than this world dreams of. Wherefore, let thy voice
Rise like a fountain for me night and day.
For what are men better than sheep or goats
That nourish a blind life within the brain,
If, knowing God, they lift not hands of prayer
Both for themselves and those who call them friend?
For so the whole round earth is every way
Bound by gold chains about the feet of God.
But now farewell. I am going a long way
With these thou seëst—if indeed I go—
(For all my mind is clouded with a doubt)
To the island-valley of Avilion;
Where falls not hail, or rain, or any snow,
Nor ever wind blows loudly; but it lies
Deep-meadow'd, happy, fair with orchard-lawns
And bowery hollows crown'd with summer sea,
Where I will heal me of my grievous wound."

So said he, and the barge with oar and sail
Moved from the brink, like some full-breasted swan
That, fluting a wild carol ere her death,
Ruffles her pure cold plume, and takes the flood
With swarthy webs. Long stood Sir Bedivere
Revolving many memories, till the hull
Look'd one black dot against the verge of dawn,
And on the mere the wailing died away.

Home-Thoughts, from Abroad

ROBERT BROWNING

Oh, to be in England
Now that April's there,
And whoever wakes in England
Sees, some morning, unaware,
That the lowest boughs and the brush-wood sheaf
Round the elm-tree bole are in tiny leaf,
While the chaffinch sings on the orchard bough
In England—now!

And after April, when May follows,
And the whitethroat builds, and all the swallows!
Hark, where my blossomed pear-tree in the hedge
Leans to the field and scatters on the clover
Blossoms and dewdrops—at the bent spray's edge—
That's the wise thrush; he sings each song twice over,
Lest you should think he never could recapture
The first fine careless rapture!
And though the fields look rough with hoary dew,
All will be gay when noontide wakes anew
The buttercups, the little children's dower
—Far brighter than this gaudy melon-flower!

Home-Thoughts, from the Sea

ROBERT BROWNING

Nobly, nobly Cape Saint Vincent to the North-West died
away;
Sunset ran, one glorious blood-red, reeking into Cadiz Bay;
Bluish mid the burning water, full in face Trafalgar lay;

In the dimmest North-East distance, dawned Gibraltar
    grand and grey;
" Here and here did England help me: how can I help
    England? "—say,
Whoso turns as I, this evening, turn to God to praise and
    pray,
While Jove's planet rises yonder, silent over Africa.

The Pied Piper of Hamelin

ROBERT BROWNING

I

HAMELIN town's in Brunswick,
  By famous Hanover city;
The River Weser, deep and wide,
Washes its walls on the southern side;
A pleasanter spot you never spied:
  But, when begins my ditty,
Almost five hundred years ago,
To see the townsfolk suffer so
  From vermin, was a pity.

II

  Rats!
They fought the dogs and killed the cats,
  And bit the babies in the cradles,
And ate the cheeses out of the vats,
  And licked the soup from the cooks' own ladles,
Split open the kegs of salted sprats,
Made nests inside men's Sunday hats,
And even spoiled the women's chats,
  By drowning their speaking
  With shrieking and squeaking
In fifty different sharps and flats.

III

At last the people in a body
 To the Town Hall came flocking:
" 'Tis clear," cried they, " our Mayor's a noddy
And as for our Corporation—shocking
To think we buy gowns lined with ermine
For dolts that can't or won't determine
What's best to rid us of our vermin!
You hope, because you're old and obese,
To find in the furry civic robe ease!
Rouse up, Sirs! Give your brains a racking
To find the remedy we're lacking,
Or, sure as fate, we'll send you packing! "
At this the Mayor and Corporation
Quaked with a mighty consternation.

IV

An hour they sat in Council;
At length the Mayor broke silence:
" For a guilder I'd my ermine gown sell—
I wish I were a mile hence!
It's easy to bid one rack one's brain—
I'm sure my poor head aches again,
I've scratched it so, and all in vain.
Oh, for a trap, a trap, a trap! "
Just as he said this, what should hap,
At the chamber door, but a gentle tap.
" Bless us! " cried the Mayor, " what's that! "
(With the Corporation as he sat,
Looking little though wondrous fat;
Nor brighter was his eye, nor moister
Than a too-long-opened oyster,
Save when at noon his paunch grew mutinous
For a plate of turtle, green and glutinous.)

" Only a scraping of shoes on the mat!
Anything like the sound of a rat
Makes my heart go pit-a-pat! "

v

" Come in! " the Mayor cried, looking bigger,
And in did come the strangest figure!
His queer long coat, from heel to head,
Was half of yellow and half of red;
And he himself was tall and thin,
With sharp blue eyes, each like a pin,
And light loose hair, yet swarthy skin,
No tuft on cheek nor beard on chin,
But lips where smiles went out and in;
There was no guessing his kith and kin.
And nobody could enough admire
The tall man and his quaint attire.
Quoth one: " It's as if my great grandsire,
Starting up at the Trump of Doom's tone,
Had walked this way from his painted tombstone! "

vi

He advanced to the council table:
And, " Please your honours," said he, " I'm able,
By means of a secret charm, to draw
All creatures living beneath the sun
That creep, or swim, or fly, or run,
After me so as you never saw!
And I chiefly use my charm
On creatures that do people harm,—
The mole, the toad, the newt, the viper:
And people call me the Pied Piper."
(And here they noticed round his neck
A scarf of red and yellow stripe,
To match his coat of the self-same cheque,
And at the scarf's end hung a pipe;

And his fingers, they noticed, were ever straying
As if impatient to be playing
Upon his pipe, as low it dangled
Over his vesture so old-fangled.)
" Yet," said he, " poor piper as I am,
In Tartary I freed the Cham,
Last June, from his huge swarms of gnats;
I eased in Asia the Nizam
Of a monstrous brood of vampyre bats;
And as for what your brain bewilders,
If I can rid your town of rats
Will you give me a thousand guilders? "
" One! fifty thousand! " was the exclamation
Of the astonished Mayor and Corporation.

VII

Into the street the Piper stept,
    Smiling first a little smile,
As if he knew what magic slept
    In his quiet pipe the while;
Then, like a musical adept,
To blow the pipe his lips he wrinkled,
And green and blue his sharp eyes twinkled,
Like a candle-flame where salt is sprinkled;
And ere three shrill notes the pipe uttered,
You heard as if an army muttered;
And the muttering grew to a grumbling;
And the grumbling grew to a mighty rumbling;
And out of the houses the rats came tumbling;
Great rats, small rats, lean rats, brawny rats,
Brown rats, black rats, grey rats, tawny rats,
Grave old plodders, gay young friskers,
    Fathers, mothers, uncles, cousins,
Cocking tails, and pricking whiskers,
    Families by tens and dozens;

Brothers, sisters, husbands, wives—
Followed the Piper for their lives.
From street to street he piped advancing,
And step for step they followed dancing,
Until they came to the River Weser,
Wherein all plunged and perished!
—Save one, who, stout as Julius Cæsar,
Swam across and lived to carry
(As he, the manuscript he cherished)
To Rat-land home his commentary:
Which was, " At the first shrill notes of the pipe
I heard a sound as of scraping tripe,
And putting apples, wondrous ripe,
Into a cider-press's gripe:
And a moving away of pickle-tub boards,
And a leaving ajar of conserve-cupboards,
And a drawing the corks of train-oil-flasks,
And a breaking the hoops of butter-casks;
And it seemed as if a voice
(Sweeter far than by harp or by psaltery
Is breathed) called out, ' Oh, rats, rejoice!
The world is grown to one vast drysaltery!
So munch on, crunch on, take your nuncheon,
Breakfast, dinner, supper, luncheon! '
And just as a bulky sugar-puncheon,
All ready staved, like a great sun shone
Glorious, scarce an inch before me,
Just as methought it said, ' Come, bore me!
—I found the Weser rolling o'er me."

VIII

You should have heard the Hamelin people
Ringing the bells till they rocked the steeple.
" Go," cried the Mayor, " and get long poles,
Poke out the nests, and block up the holes!

Consult with carpenters and builders,
And leave in our town not even a trace
Of the rats!" When suddenly, up the face
Of the Piper perked in the market-place,
With a " First, if you please, my thousand guilders! "

IX

A thousand guilders! The Mayor looked blue;
So did the Corporation, too.
For council dinners made rare havoc
With Claret, Moselle, Vin-de-Grave, Hock;
And half the money would replenish
Their cellar's biggest butt with Rhenish.
To pay this sum to a wandering fellow,
With a gipsy coat of red and yellow!
" Beside," quoth the Mayor, with a knowing wink,
" Our business was done at the river's brink;
We saw with our eyes the vermin sink,
And what's dead can't come to life, I think.
So friend, we're not the folks to shrink
From the duty of giving you something for drink,
And a matter of money to put in your poke;
But, as for the guilders, what we spoke
Of them, as you very well know, was in joke.
Besides, our losses have made us thrifty.
A thousand guilders! come, take fifty! "

X

The Piper's face fell, and he cried,
" No trifling! I can't wait, beside!
I've promised to visit by dinner-time
Bagdad, and accept the prime
Of the Head-Cook's pottage, all he's rich in,
For having left, in the Caliph's kitchen,

Of a nest of scorpions no survivor.
With him I proved no bargain-driver;
With you, don't think I'll bate a stiver!
And folks who put me in a passion
May find me pipe to another fashion."

XI

" How! " cried the Mayor, " d'ye think I'll brook
Being worse treated than a cook?
Insulted by a lazy ribald
With idle pipe and vesture piebald!
You threaten us, fellow!   Do your worst!
Blow your pipe there till you burst! "

XII

Once more he stept into the street,
    And to his lips again
Laid his long pipe of smooth, straight cane;
    And ere he blew three notes (such sweet,
Soft notes as yet musician's cunning
    Never gave the enraptured air)
There was a rustling that seemed like a bustling
Of merry crowds justling at pitching and hustling,
Small feet were pattering, wooden shoes clattering,
Little hands clapping and little tongues chattering,
And, like fowls in a farmyard when barley is scattering,
    Out came the children running.
    All the little boys and girls,
    With rosy cheeks and flaxen curls,
    And sparkling eyes and teeth like pearls,
Tripping and skipping ran merrily after
The wonderful music with shouting and laughter.

XIII

The Mayor was dumb, and the Council stood
As if they were changed into blocks of wood,
Unable to move a step, or cry
To the children merrily skipping by
—And could only follow with the eye
That joyous crowd at the Piper's back.
And now the Mayor was on the rack,
And the wretched Council's bosoms beat,
As the Piper turned from the High Street
To where the Weser rolled its waters
Right in the way of their sons and daughters!
However he turned from South to West,
And to Koppelberg Hill his steps addressed,
And after him the children pressed;
Great was the joy in every breast.
" He never can cross that mighty top!
He's forced to let the piping drop,
And we shall see our children stop! "
When, lo, as they reached the mountain-side,
A wondrous portal opened wide,
As if a cavern was suddenly hollowed;
And the Piper advanced, and the children followed,
And when all were in to the very last,
The door in the mountain-side shut fast.
Did I say all? No! One was lame,
And could not dance the whole of the way;
And in after-years, if you would blame
His sadness, he was used to say,—
" It's dull in our town since my playmates left!
I can't forget that I'm bereft
Of all the pleasant sights they see,
Which the Piper also promised me:
For he led us, he said, to a joyous land,
Joining the town and just at hand,

Where waters gushed and fruit trees grew,
And flowers put forth a fairer hue,
And everything was strange and new;
The sparrows were brighter than peacocks here,
And their dogs outran our fallow-deer,
And honey-bees had lost their stings,
And horses were born with eagles' wings:
And just as I became assured
My lame foot would be speedily cured,
The music stopped, and I stood still,
And found myself outside the hill,
Left alone against my will,
To go now limping as before,
And never hear of that country more! "

XIV

Alas, alas for Hamelin!
   There came into many a burgher's pate
   A text which says that Heaven's gate
   Opes to the rich at as easy rate
As the needle's eye takes a camel in!

The Mayor sent East, West, North, and South,
To offer the Piper, by word of mouth,
   Wherever it was men's lot to find him,
Silver and gold to his heart's content,
If he'd only return the way he went,
   And bring the children behind him.
But when they saw 'twas a lost endeavour,
And Piper and dancers were gone for ever,
They made a decree that lawyers never
   Should think their records dated duly
If, after the day of the month and the year,
These words did not as well appear:
" And so long after what happened here

On the twenty-second of July,
Thirteen hundred and seventy-six: "
And the better in memory to fix
The place of the children's last retreat,
They called it, the Pied Piper's Street—
Where anyone playing on pipe or tabor
Was sure for the future to lose his labour.
Nor suffered they hostelry or tavern
   To shock with mirth a street so solemn;
But opposite the place of the cavern
   They wrote the story on a column,
And on the great church-window painted
The same, to make the world acquainted
How their children were stolen away;
And there it stands to this very day.
And I must not omit to say
That in Transylvania there's a tribe
Of alien people that ascribe
The outlandish ways and dress,
On which their neighbours lay such stress,
To their fathers and mothers having risen
Out of some subterranean prison
Into which they were trepanned,
Long time ago in a mighty band,
Out of Hamelin town in Brunswick land,
But how or why, they don't understand.

xv

So, Willy, let you and me be wipers
Of scores out with all men, especially pipers!
And, whether they pipe us free from rats or from mice,
If we've promised them aught, let us keep our promise!

The Ocean

LORD BYRON

Roll on, thou deep and dark blue Ocean—roll!
Ten thousand fleets sweep over thee in vain;
Man marks the earth with ruin—his control
Stops with the shore;—upon the watery plain
The wrecks are all thy deed, nor doth remain
A shadow of man's ravage, save his own,
When, for a moment, like a drop of rain,
He sinks into thy depths with bubbling groan—
Without a grave—unknelled, uncoffined, and unknown.

His steps are not upon thy paths,—thy fields
Are not a spoil for him,—thou dost arise
And shake him from thee; the vile strength he wields
For Earth's destruction thou dost all despise,
Spurning him from thy bosom to the skies—
And send'st him, shivering in thy playful spray
And howling, to his Gods, where haply lies
His petty hope in some near port or bay,
And dashest him again to Earth:—there let him lay.

The armaments which thunderstrike the walls
Of rock-built cities, bidding nations quake,
And Monarchs tremble in their Capitals,
The oak Leviathans, whose huge ribs make
Their clay creator the vain title take
Of Lord of thee, and Arbiter of War—
These are thy toys, and, as the snowy flake,
They melt into thy yeast of waves, which mar
Alike the Armada's pride, or spoils of Trafalgar.

Thy shores are empires, changed in all save thee—
Assyria—Greece—Rome—Carthage—what are they?
Thy waters washed them power while they were free,
And many a tyrant since; their shores obey
The stranger, slave, or savage; their decay
Has dried up realms to deserts:—not so thou,
Unchangeable save to thy wild waves' play;
Time writes no wrinkle on thine azure brow—
Such as Creation's dawn beheld, thou rollest now.

Thou glorious mirror, where the Almighty's form
Glasses itself in tempests; in all time,
Calm or convulsed—in breeze, or gale, or storm—
Icing the Pole, or in the torrid clime
Dark-heaving—boundless, endless, and sublime—
The image of Eternity—the throne
Of the Invisible; even from out thy slime
The monsters of the deep are made—each Zone
Obeys thee—thou goest forth, dread, fathomless, alone.

And I have loved thee, Ocean! and my joy
Of youthful sports was on thy breast to be
Borne, like thy bubbles, onward: from a boy
I wantoned with thy breakers—they to me
Were a delight; and if the freshening sea
Made them a terror—'twas a pleasing fear,
For I was as it were a Child of thee,
And trusted to thy billows far and near,
And laid my hand upon thy mane—as I do here.

The Village Preacher

OLIVER GOLDSMITH

NEAR yonder copse, where once the garden smiled,
And still where many a garden flower grows wild;
There, where a few torn shrubs the place disclose,
The village preacher's modest mansion rose.
A man he was to all the country dear,
And passing rich with forty pounds a year;
Remote from towns he ran his godly race,
Nor e'er had changed, nor wished to change, his place;
Unskilful he to fawn, or seek for power,
By doctrines fashion'd to the varying hour;
Far other aims his heart had learnt to prize,
More bent to raise the wretched than to rise.
His house was known to all the vagrant train,
He chid their wanderings, but relieved their pain;
The long-remembered beggar was his guest,
Whose beard descending swept his aged breast;
The ruin'd spendthrift, now no longer proud,
Claim'd kindred there, and had his claims allow'd;
The broken soldier, kindly bade to stay,
Sat by his fire, and talk'd the night away;
Wept o'er his wounds, or tales of sorrow done,
Shoulder'd his crutch, and showed how fields were won.
Pleased with his guests, the good man learn'd to glow,
And quite forgot their vices in their woe;
Careless their merits or their faults to scan,
His pity gave ere charity began.
    Thus to relieve the wretched was his pride,
And e'en his failings lean'd to virtue's side;
But in his duty prompt at every call,
He watch'd and wept, he pray'd and felt for all;

And, as a bird each fond endearment tries,
To tempt its new fledged offspring to the skies,
He tried each art, reproved each dull delay,
Allured to brighter worlds, and led the way.

    Beside the bed where parting life was laid,
And sorrow, guilt, and pain, by turns dismay'd,
The reverend champion stood.   At his control,
Despair and anguish fled the struggling soul;
Comfort came down the trembling wretch to raise,
And his last faltering accents whispered praise.

    At church, with meek and unaffected grace,
His looks adorn'd the venerable place;
Truth from his lips prevail'd with double sway,
And fools, who came to scoff, remain'd to pray.
The service past, around the pious man,
With steady zeal, each honest rustic ran;
E'en children follow'd with endearing wile,
And pluck'd his gown, to share the good man's smile
His ready smile a parent's warmth express'd,
Their welfare pleased him, and their cares distress'd;
To them his heart, his love, his griefs were given,
But all his serious thoughts had rest in heaven.
As some tall cliff that lifts its awful form,
Swells from the vale, and midway leaves the storm,
Though round its breast the rolling clouds are spread
Eternal sunshine settles on its head.

The Village Schoolmaster

OLIVER GOLDSMITH

    BESIDE yon straggling fence that skirts the way,
With blossom'd furze unprofitably gay,
There, in his noisy mansion, skill'd to rule,
The village master taught his little school:

A man severe he was, and stern to view,
I knew him well, and every truant knew:
Well had the boding tremblers learn'd to trace
The day's disasters in his morning face;
Full well they laugh'd with counterfeited glee
At all his jokes, for many a joke had he;
Full well the busy whisper circling round,
Convey'd the dismal tidings when he frown'd:
Yet he was kind, or if severe in aught,
The love he bore to learning was in fault;
The village all declared how much he knew,
'Twas certain he could write, and cipher too;
Lands he could measure, terms and tides presage,
And e'en the story ran—that he could gauge:
In arguing too, the parson own'd his skill,
For e'en though vanquish'd, he could argue still;
While words of learned length, and thundering sound,
Amazed the gazing rustics ranged around;
And still they gazed, and still the wonder grew
That one small head could carry all he knew.

Elegy on the Death of a Mad Dog

OLIVER GOLDSMITH

Good people all of every sort,
   Give ear unto my song;
And if you find it wondrous short,
   It cannot hold you long.

In Islington there was a man,
   Of whom the world might say,
That still a godly race he ran,
   Whene'er he went to pray.

A kind and gentle heart he had,
　To comfort friends and foes:
The naked every day he clad,
　When he put on his clothes.

And in that town a dog was found,
　As many dogs there be,
Both mongrel, puppy, whelp, and hound,
　And curs of low degree.

The dog and man at first were friends;
　But when a pique began,
The dog, to gain some private ends,
　Went mad and bit the man.

Around from all the neighb'ring streets
　The wond'ring neighbours ran,
And swore the dog had lost its wits,
　To bite so good a man.

The wound it seemed both sore and sad,
　To every Christian eye;
And while they swore the dog was mad,
　They swore the man would die.

But soon a wonder came to light
　That showed the rogues they lied:
The man recovered of his bite,
　The dog it was that died.

A New Jerusalem

WILLIAM BLAKE

AND did those feet in ancient time
Walk upon England's mountains green:
And was the holy Lamb of God
On England's pleasant pastures seen?

And did the Countenance Divine
Shine forth upon our clouded hills?
And was Jerusalem builded here,
Among these dark Satanic Mills?

Bring me my Bow of burning gold:
Bring me my Arrows of desire:
Bring me my Spear: O clouds unfold:
Bring me my Chariot of fire!

I will not cease from Mental Fight,
Nor shall my Sword sleep in my hand:
Till we have built Jerusalem,
In England's green and pleasant Land.

Night

WILLIAM BLAKE

THE sun descending in the west,
　The evening star does shine;
The birds are silent in their nest,
　And I must seek for mine.

F

M.V

The moon, like a flower,
In heaven's high bower,
With silent delight
Sits and smiles on the night.

Farewell, green fields and happy groves,
    Where flocks have took delight;
Where lambs have nibbled, silent moves
    The feet of angels bright;
        Unseen they pour blessing,
        And joy without ceasing,
        On each bud and blossom,
        And each sleeping bosom.

They look in every thoughtless nest
    Where birds are covered warm;
They visit caves of every beast,
    To keep them all from harm.
        If they see any weeping
        That should have been sleeping,
        They pour sleep on their head,
        And sit down by their bed.

When wolves and tigers howl for prey,
    They pitying stand and weep,
Seeking to drive their thirst away,
    And keep them from the sheep.
        But if they rush dreadful,
        The angels, most heedful,
        Receive each mild spirit,
        New worlds to inherit.

And there the lion's ruddy eyes
    Shall flow with tears of gold,
And pitying the tender cries,
    And walking round the fold,

Saying: " Wrath, by His meekness,
And, by His health, sickness
Is driven away
From our immortal day.

" And now beside thee, bleating lamb,
    I can lie down and sleep;
Or think on Him who bore thy name,
    Graze after thee, and weep.
                For wash'd in life's river
                My bright mane for ever
                Shall shine like the gold
                As I guard o'er the fold."

The Tiger

WILLIAM BLAKE

TIGER, tiger, burning bright
In the forests of the night,
What immortal hand or eye
Could frame thy fearful symmetry?

In what distant deeps or skies
Burnt the fire of thine eyes?
On what wings dare he aspire?
What the hand dare seize the fire?

And what shoulder and what art
Could twist the sinews of thy heart?
And, when thy heart began to beat,
What dread hand and what dread feet?

What the hammer? what the chain?
In what furnace was thy brain?
What the anvil? what dread grasp
Dare its deadly terrors clasp?

When the stars threw down their spears,
And watered heaven with their tears,
Did He smile his work to see?
Did He who made the lamb make thee?

Tiger, tiger, burning bright
In the forests of the night,
What immortal hand or eye
Dare frame thy fearful symmetry?

The Rime of the Ancient Mariner
(abridged)

SAMUEL T. COLERIDGE

PART I

IT is an ancient Mariner,
And he stoppeth one of three.
" By thy long grey beard and glittering eye,
Now wherefore stopp'st thou me?

The Bridegroom's doors are opened wide,
And I am next of kin;
The guests are met, the feast is set;
May'st hear the merry din."

He holds him with his skinny hand,
" There was a ship," quoth he.
" Hold off! unhand me, grey-beard loon! "
Eftsoons his hand dropt he.

He holds him with his glittering eye—
The Wedding-Guest stood still,
And listens like a three years' child:
The Mariner hath his will.

The Wedding-Guest sat on a stone:
He cannot choose but hear;
And thus spake on that ancient man,
The bright-eyed Mariner.

" The ship was cheered, the harbour cleared,
Merrily did we drop
Below the kirk, below the hill,
Below the lighthouse top.

The sun came up upon the left,
Out of the sea came he!
And he shone bright, and on the right
Went down into the sea.

Higher and higher every day,
Till over the mast at noon— "
The Wedding-Guest here beat his breast,
For he heard the loud bassoon.

The bride hath paced into the hall,
Red as a rose is she;
Nodding their heads before her goes
The merry minstrelsy.

The Wedding-Guest he beat his breast,
Yet he cannot choose but hear;
And thus spake on that ancient man,
The bright-eyed Mariner.

" And now the Storm-blast came, and he
Was tyrannous and strong:
He struck with his o'ertaking wings,
And chased us south along.

With sloping masts and dipping prow,
As who pursued with yell and blow
Still treads the shadow of his foe,
And forward bends his head,
The ship drove fast, loud roared the blast,
And Southward aye we fled.

And now there came both mist and snow,
And it grew wondrous cold:
And ice, mast-high, came floating by,
As green as emerald.

And through the drifts the snowy clifts
Did send a dismal sheen:
Nor shapes of men nor beasts we ken—
The ice was all between.

The ice was here, the ice was there,
The ice was all around:
It cracked and growled, and roared and howled,
Like noises in a swound!

At length did cross an Albatross,
Thorough the fog it came;
As if it had been a Christian soul,
We hailed it in God's name.

It ate the food it ne'er had eat,
And round and round it flew.
The ice did split with a thunder-fit
The helmsman steered us through

And a good south wind sprung up behind;
The Albatross did follow,
And every day, for food or play,
Came to the mariners' hollo!

In mist or cloud, on mast or shroud,
It perched for vespers nine;
Whiles all the night, through fog-smoke white,
Glimmered the white moon-shine."

" God save thee, ancient Mariner!
From the fiends, that plague thee thus!—
Why look'st thou so? "—" With my cross-bow
I shot the Albatross.

PART II

" The Sun now rose upon the right:
Out of the sea came he,
Still hid in mist, and on the left
Went down into the sea.

And the good south wind still blew behind,
But no sweet bird did follow,
Nor any day for food or play
Came to the mariners' hollo!

And I had done a hellish thing,
And it would work 'em woe:
For all averred, I had killed the bird
That made the breeze to blow.
Ah wretch! said they, the bird to slay,
That made the breeze to blow!

Nor dim nor red, like God's own head,
The glorious Sun uprist:
Then all averred, I had killed the bird
That brought the fog and mist.
'Twas right, said they, such birds to slay,
That bring the fog and mist.

The fair breeze blew, the white foam flew,
The furrow followed free;
We were the first that ever burst
Into that silent sea.

Down dropt the breeze, the sails dropt down,
'Twas sad as sad could be;
And we did speak only to break
The silence of the sea!

All in a hot and copper sky,
The bloody Sun, at noon,
Right up above the mast did stand,
No bigger than the Moon.

Day after day, day after day,
We stuck, nor breath nor motion;
As idle as a painted ship
Upon a painted ocean.

Water, water, every where,
And all the boards did shrink;
Water, water, every where,
Nor any drop to drink.

The very deep did rot: O Christ!
That ever this should be!
Yea, slimy things did crawl with legs
Upon the slimy sea.

About, about, in reel and rout
The death-fires danced at night;
The water, like a witch's oils,
Burnt green, and blue and white.

And some in dreams assuréd were
Of the Spirit that plagued us so;
Nine fathom deep he had followed us
From the land of mist and snow.

And every tongue, through utter drought,
Was withered at the root;
We could not speak, no more than if
We had been choked with soot.

Ah! well a-day! what evil looks
Had I from old and young!
Instead of the cross, the Albatross
About my neck was hung.

PART III

" There passed a weary time.   Each throat
Was parched, and glazed each eye.
A weary time! a weary time!
How glazed each weary eye,
When looking westward, I beheld
A something in the sky.

At first it seemed a little speck,
And then it seemed a mist;
It moved and moved, and took at last
A certain shape, I wist.

A speck, a mist, a shape, I wist!
And still it neared and neared:
As if it dodged a water-sprite,
It plunged and tack'd and veered.

With throats unslaked, with black lips baked,
We could nor laugh nor wail;
Through utter drought all dumb we stood!
I bit my arm, I sucked the blood,
And cried, A sail! a sail!

With throats unslaked, with black lips baked,
Agape they heard me call:
Gramercy! they for joy did grin,
And all at once their breath drew in,
As they were drinking all.

See! see! (I cried) she tacks no more!
Hither to work us weal;
Without a breeze, without a tide,
She steadies with upright keel!

The western wave was all a-flame.
The day was well nigh done!
Almost upon the western wave
Rested the broad bright Sun;
When that strange shape drove suddenly
Betwixt us and the Sun.

And straight the Sun was flecked with bars,
(Heaven's Mother send us grace!)
As if through a dungeon-grate he peered
With broad and burning face.

Alas! (thought I, and my heart beat loud)
How fast she nears and nears!
Are those her sails that glance in the Sun,
Like restless gossameres?

Are those her ribs through which the Sun
Did peer, as through a grate?
And is that Woman all her crew?
Is that a Death? and are there two?
Is Death that woman's mate?

Her lips were red, her looks were free,
Her locks were yellow as gold:
Her skin was as white as leprosy,
The Night-Mare Life-in-Death was she,
Who thicks man's blood with cold.

The naked hulk alongside came,
And the twain were casting dice;
' The game is done!   I've won!   I've won! '
Quoth she, and whistles thrice.

The Sun's rim dips; the stars rush out:
At one stride comes the dark;
With far-heard whisper, o'er the sea,
Off shot the spectre-bark.

We listened and looked sideways up!
Fear at my heart, as at a cup,
My life-blood seemed to sip!
The stars were dim, and thick the night,
The steersman's face by his lamp gleamed white
From the sails the dew did drip—
Till clomb above the eastern bar
The hornéd moon, with one bright star
Within the nether tip.

One after one, by the star-dogged Moon,
Too quick for groan or sigh,
Each turned his face with a ghastly pang,
And cursed me with his eye.

Four times fifty living men,
(And I heard nor sigh nor groan)
With heavy thump, a lifeless lump,
They dropped down one by one.

The souls did from their bodies fly,—
They fled to bliss or woe!
And every soul, it passed me by,
Like the whizz of my cross-bow!"

PART IV

" I fear thee, ancient Mariner!
I fear thy skinny hand!
And thou art long, and lank, and brown,
As is the ribbed sea-sand.

I fear thee and thy glittering eye,
And thy skinny hand, so brown."—
" Fear not, fear not, thou Wedding-Guest!
This body dropt not down.

Alone, alone, all, all alone,
Alone on a wide wide sea!
And never a saint took pity on
My soul in agony.

The many men, so beautiful!
And they all dead did lie:
And a thousand thousand slimy things
Lived on; and so did I.

I looked upon the rotting sea,
And drew my eyes away;
I looked upon the rotting deck,
And there the dead men lay.

I looked to heaven, and tried to pray;
But or ever a prayer had gusht,
A wicked whisper came, and made
My heart as dry as dust.

I closed my lids, and kept them close,
And the balls like pulses beat;
For the sky and the sea, and the sea and the sky
Lay like a load on my weary eye,
And the dead were at my feet.

The cold sweat melted from their limbs,
Nor rot nor reek did they:
The look with which they looked on me
Had never passed away.

An orphan's curse would drag to hell
A spirit from on high;
But oh! more horrible than that
Is a curse in a dead man's eye!
Seven days, seven nights, I saw that curse,
And yet I could not die.

The moving Moon went up the sky,
And no where did abide:
Softly she was going up,
And a star or two beside—

Her beams bemocked the sultry main,
Like April hoar-frost spread;
But where the ship's huge shadow lay,
The charmed water burnt alway
A still and awful red.

Beyond the shadow of the ship,
I watched the water-snakes:
They moved in tracks of shining white,
And when they reared, the elfish light
Fell off in hoary flakes.

Within the shadow of the ship
I watched their rich attire:
Blue, glossy green, and velvet black,
They coiled and swam; and every track
Was a flash of golden fire.

O happy living things! no tongue
Their beauty might declare:
A spring of love gushed from my heart,
And I blessed them unaware:
Sure my kind saint took pity on me,
And I blessed them unaware.

The selfsame moment I could pray;
And from my neck so free
The Albatross fell off, and sank
Like lead into the sea.

PART V

"Oh sleep! it is a gentle thing,
Beloved from pole to pole!
To Mary Queen the praise be given!
She sent the gentle sleep from Heaven,
That slid into my soul.

The silly buckets on the deck,
That had so long remained,
I dreamt that they were filled with dew;
And when I awoke, it rained.

My lips were wet, my throat was cold,
My garments all were dank;
Sure I had drunken in my dreams,
And still my body drank.

I moved, and could not feel my limbs:
I was so light—almost
I thought that I had died in sleep,
And was a blessed ghost.

And soon I heard a roaring wind:
It did not come anear;
But with its sound it shook the sails,
That were so thin and sere.

The upper air burst into life!
And a hundred fire-flags sheen,
To and fro they were hurried about!
And to and fro, and in and out,
The wan stars danced between.

And the coming wind did roar more loud,
And the sails did sigh like sedge;
And the rain poured down from one black cloud;
The Moon was at its edge.

The thick black cloud was cleft, and still
The Moon was at its side:
Like waters shot from some high crag,
The lightning fell with never a jag,
A river steep and wide.

The loud wind never reached the ship,
Yet now the ship moved on!
Beneath the lightning and the Moon
The dead men gave a groan.

They groaned, they stirred, they all uprose,
Nor spake, nor moved their eyes;
It had been strange, even in a dream,
To have seen those dead men rise.

The helmsman steered, the ship moved on;
Yet never a breeze up blew;
The mariners all 'gan work the ropes,
Where they were wont to do;
They raised their limbs like lifeless tools—
We were a ghastly crew.

The body of my brother's son
Stood by me, knee to knee:
The body and I pulled at one rope
But he said nought to me."

" I fear thee, ancient Mariner! "
" Be calm, thou Wedding-Guest!
'Twas not those souls that fled in pain,
Which to their corses came again,
But a troop of spirits blest:

For when it dawned—they dropped their arms,
And clustered round the mast;
Sweet sounds rose slowly through their mouths,
And from their bodies passed.

Around, around, flew each sweet sound,
Then darted to the Sun;
Slowly the sounds came back again,
Now mixed, now one by one.

Sometimes a-dropping from the sky
I heard the sky-lark sing;
Sometimes all little birds that are,
How they seemed to fill the sea and air
With their sweet jargoning!

And now 'twas like all instruments,
Now like a lonely flute;
And now it is an angel's song,
That makes the heavens be mute.

It ceased; yet still the sails made on
A pleasant noise till noon,
A noise like of a hidden brook
In the leafy month of June,
That to the sleeping woods all night
Singeth a quiet tune.

Till noon we quietly sailed on,
Yet never a breeze did breathe:
Slowly and smoothly went the ship,
Moved onward from beneath.

Under the keel nine fathom deep,
From the land of mist and snow,
The spirit slid: and it was he
That made the ship to go.
The sails at noon left off their tune,
And the ship stood still also.

The Sun, right up above the mast,
Had fixed her to the ocean:
But in a minute she 'gan stir,
With a short uneasy motion—
Backwards and forwards half her length
With a short uneasy motion.

Then like a pawing horse let go,
She made a sudden bound:
It flung the blood into my head,
And I fell down in a swound.

How long in that same fit I lay,
I have not to declare;
But ere my living life returned,
I heard and in my soul discerned
Two voices in the air.

' Is it he? ' quoth one, ' Is this the man?
By him who died on cross,
With his cruel bow he laid full low
The harmless Albatross.

The spirit who bideth by himself
In the land of mist and snow,
He loved the bird that loved the man
Who shot him with his bow.'

The other was a softer voice,
As soft as honey-dew:
Quoth he, ' The man hath penance done,
And penance more will do.'

PART VI

" I woke, and we were sailing on
As in a gentle weather:
'Twas night, calm night, the moon was high,
The dead men stood together.

All stood together on the deck,
For a charnel-dungeon fitter:
All fixed on me their stony eyes,
That in the Moon did glitter.

The pang, the curse, with which they died,
Had never passed away:
I could not draw my eyes from theirs,
Nor turn them up to pray.

And now this spell was snapt: once more
I viewed the ocean green,
And looked far forth, yet little saw
Of what had else been seen—

Like one, that on a lonesome road
Doth walk in fear and dread,
And having once turned round walks on,
And turns no more his head;
Because he knows, a frightful fiend
Doth close behind him tread.

But soon there breathed a wind on me,
Nor sound nor motion made:
Its path was not upon the sea,
In ripple or in shade.

It raised my hair, it fanned my cheek
Like a meadow-gale of spring—
It mingled strangely with my fears,
Yet it felt like a welcoming.

Swiftly, swiftly flew the ship,
Yet she sailed softly too:
Sweetly, sweetly blew the breeze—
On me alone it blew.

Oh! dream of joy! is this indeed
The light-house top I see?
Is this the hill? is this the kirk?
Is this mine own countree?

We drifted o'er the harbour-bar,
And I with sobs did pray—
O let me be awake, my God!
Or let me sleep away.

The harbour-bay was clear as glass,
So smoothly it was strewn!
And on the bay the moonlight lay,
And the shadow of the Moon.

The rock shone bright, the kirk no less,
That stands above the rock:
The moonlight steeped in silentness
The steady weathercock.

And the bay was white with silent light
Till rising from the same,
Full many shapes, that shadows were,
In crimson colours came.

.   .   .   .   .   .

But soon I heard the dash of oars,
I heard the Pilot's cheer;
My head was turned perforce away,
And I saw a boat appear.

The Pilot and the Pilot's boy,
I heard them coming fast:
Dear Lord in Heaven! it was a joy
The dead men could not blast.

I saw a third—I heard his voice:
It is the Hermit good!
He singeth loud his godly hymns
That he makes in the wood.
He'll shrieve my soul, he'll wash away
The Albatross's blood.

PART VII

"This Hermit good lives in the wood
Which slopes down to the sea.
How loudly his sweet voice he rears!
He loves to talk with mariners
That come from a far countree.

He kneels at morn, and noon, and eve—
He hath a cushion plump:
It is the moss that wholly hides
The rotted old oak-stump.

.   .   .   .   .   .

' O shrieve me, shrieve me, holy man! '
The Hermit crossed his brow.
' Say quick,' quoth he, ' I bid thee say—
What manner of man art thou? '

Forthwith this frame of mine was wrenched
With a woful agony,
Which forced me to begin my tale;
And then it left me free.

Since then, at an uncertain hour,
That agony returns:
And till my ghastly tale is told,
This heart within me burns.

I pass, like night, from land to land;
I have strange power of speech;
That moment that his face I see,
I know the man that must hear me:
To him my tale I teach.

What loud uproar bursts from that door!
The wedding-guests are there:
But in the garden-bower the bride
And bride-maids singing are:
And hark the little vesper bell,
Which biddeth me to prayer!

O Wedding-Guest! this soul hath been
Alone on a wide wide sea:
So lonely 'twas, that God himself
Scarce seeméd there to be.

O sweeter than the marriage-feast,
'Tis sweeter far to me,
To walk together to the kirk
With a goodly company!—

To walk together to the kirk,
And all together pray,
While each to his great Father bends,
Old men, and babes, and loving friends,
And youths and maidens gay!

Farewell, farewell! but this I tell
To thee, thou Wedding-Guest!
He prayeth well, who loveth well
Both man and bird and beast.

He prayeth best, who loveth best
All things both great and small;
For the dear God who loveth us,
He made and loveth all."

The Mariner, whose eye is bright,
Whose beard with age is hoar,
Is gone: and now the Wedding-Guest
Turned from the bridegroom's door.

He went like one that hath been stunned,
And is of sense forlorn:
A sadder and a wiser man,
He rose the morrow morn.

England, with all thy Faults

WILLIAM COWPER

ENGLAND, with all thy faults, I love thee still,
My country! and, while yet a nook is left
Where English minds and manners may be found,
Shall be constrained to love thee.   Though thy clime
Be fickle, and thy year, most part, deformed
With dripping rains, or withered by a frost,
I would not yet exchange thy sullen skies
And fields without a flower, for warmer France
With all her vines; nor for Ausonia's groves
Of golden fruitage, and her myrtle bowers.
To shake thy senate, and from heights sublime
Of patriot eloquence to flash down fire
Upon thy foes, was never meant my task;
But I can feel thy fortunes, and partake
Thy joys and sorrows with as true a heart
As any thunderer there.   And I can feel
Thy follies too, and with a just disdain
Frown at effeminates, whose very looks
Reflect dishonour on the land I love.
How, in the name of soldiership and sense,
Should England prosper, when such things, as smooth

And tender as a girl, all-essenced o'er
With odours, and as profligate as sweet,
Who sell their laurel for a myrtle wreath,
And love when they should fight,—when such as these
Presume to lay their hand upon the ark
Of her magnificent and awful cause?
Time was when it was praise and boast enough
In every clime, and travel where we might,
That we were born her children; praise enough
To fill the ambition of a private man,
That Chatham's language was his mother tongue,
And Wolfe's great name compatriot with his own.
Farewell those honours, and farewell with them
The hope of such hereafter! They have fallen
Each in his field of glory: one in arms,
And one in council—Wolfe upon the lap
Of smiling Victory that moment won,
And Chatham, heart-sick of his country's shame!
They made us many soldiers. Chatham still
Consulting England's happiness at home,
Secured it by an unforgiving frown
If any wronged her. Wolfe, where'er he fought,
Put so much of his heart into his act,
That his example had a magnet's force,
And all were swift to follow whom all loved.
Those suns are set. Oh rise some other such!
Or all that we have left is empty talk
Of old achievements, and despair of new.

Loss of the *Royal George*

WILLIAM COWPER

TOLL for the Brave!
The brave that are no more!
  All sunk beneath the wave
Fast by their native shore!

  Eight hundred of the brave,
Whose courage well was tried,
  Had made the vessel heel
And laid her on her side.

  A land-breeze shook the shrouds
And she was overset;
  Down went the Royal George,
With all her crew complete.

  Toll for the brave!
Brave Kempenfelt is gone;
  His last sea-fight is fought.
His work of glory done.

  It was not in the battle;
No tempest gave the shock;
  She sprang no fatal leak,
She ran upon no rock.

  His sword was in the sheath,
His fingers held the pen,
  When Kempenfelt went down
With twice four hundred men.

Weigh the vessel up
Once dreaded by our foes,
   And mingle with your cup
The tears that England owes.

Her timbers yet are sound,
And she may float again
   Full charged with England's thunder,
And plough the distant main:

But Kempenfelt is gone,
His victories are o'er;
   And he and his eight hundred
Must plough the wave no more.

Boadicea

WILLIAM COWPER

WHEN the British warrior queen,
   Bleeding from the Roman rods,
Sought, with an indignant mien,
   Counsel of her country's gods,

Sage beneath a spreading oak
   Sat the Druid, hoary chief,
Every burning word he spoke
   Full of rage and full of grief:

" Princess! if our aged eyes
   Weep upon thy matchless wrongs
'Tis because resentment ties
   All the terrors of our tongues.

" Rome shall perish—write that word
   In the blood that she has spilt;
Perish hopeless and abhorred,
   Deep in ruin as in guilt.

" Rome, for empire far renowned,
   Tramples on a thousand states;
Soon her pride shall kiss the ground,—
   Hark! the Gaul is at her gates.

" Other Romans shall arise,
   Heedless of a soldier's name,
Sounds, not arms, shall win the prize,
   Harmony the path to fame.

" Then the progeny that springs
   From the forests of our land,
Armed with thunder, clad with wings,
   Shall a wider world command.

" Regions Cæsar never knew
   Thy posterity shall sway,
Where his eagles never flew,
   None invincible as they."

Such the bard's prophetic words,
   Pregnant with celestial fire,
Bending as he swept the chords
   Of his sweet but awful lyre.

She, with all a monarch's pride,
   Felt them in her bosom glow,
Rushed to battle, fought and died,
   Dying, hurled them at the foe.

" Ruffians, pitiless as proud,
    Heaven awards the vengeance due;
Empire is on us bestowed,
    Shame and ruin wait for you! "

On First Looking into Chapman's Homer

JOHN KEATS

MUCH have I travell'd in the realms of gold
    And many goodly states and kingdoms seen;
    Round many western islands have I been
Which bards in fealty to Apollo hold.
Oft of one wide expanse had I been told
    That deep-brow'd Homer ruled as his demesne;
    Yet did I never breathe its pure serene
Till I heard Chapman speak out loud and bold:
Then felt I like some watcher of the skies
    When a new planet swims into his ken;
Or like stout Cortez, when with eagle eyes
    He stared at the Pacific—and all his men
Look'd at each other with a wild surmise—
    Silent, upon a peak in Darien.

Abou Ben Adhem

LEIGH HUNT

ABOU BEN ADHEM (may his tribe increase!)
Awoke one night from a deep dream of peace,
And saw, within the moonlight in his room,
Making it rich and like a lily in bloom,

An angel writing in a book of gold.
Exceeding peace had made Ben Adhem bold,
And to the presence in the room he said,
" What writest thou? "—the vision rais'd its head,
And with a look made of all sweet accord,
Answered, " The names of those who love the Lord."
" And is mine one? " said Abou.   " Nay, not so,"
Replied the angel.   Abou spoke more low,
But cheerily still; and said, " I pray thee then,
Write me as one that loves his fellow-men."
The angel wrote, and vanish'd.   The next night
It came again with a great awakening light,
And show'd the names whom love of God had bless'd,
And lo! Ben Adhem's name led all the rest.

Full Moon

WALTER DE LA MARE

ONE night as Dick lay half asleep,
　　Into his drowsy eyes
A great still light began to creep
　　From out the silent skies.
It was the lovely moon's, for when
　　He raised his dreamy head,
Her surge of silver filled the pane
　　And streamed across his bed.
So, for a while, each gazed at each—
　　Dick and the solemn moon—
Till, climbing slowly on her way,
　　She vanished, and was gone.

Silver

WALTER DE LA MARE

SLOWLY, silently, now the moon
Walks the night in her silver shoon;
This way, and that, she peers, and sees
Silver fruit upon silver trees;
One by one the casements catch
Her beams beneath the silvery thatch;
Couched in his kennel, like a log,
With paws of silver sleeps the dog;
From their shadowy cote the white breasts peep
Of doves in a silver-feathered sleep;
A harvest mouse goes scampering by,
With silver claws, and silver eye;
And moveless fish in the water gleam,
By silver reeds in a silver stream.

I vow to thee, my Country

SIR CECIL SPRING RICE

I vow to thee, my country—all earthly things above—
Entire and whole and perfect, the service of my love,
The love that asks no questions: the love that stands the
      test,
That lays upon the altar the dearest and the best:
The love that never falters, the love that pays the price,
The love that makes undaunted the final sacrifice.

And there's another country, I've heard of long ago—
Most dear to them that love her, most great to them that
      know—

We may not count her armies: we may not see her
     king—
Her fortress is a faithful heart, her pride is suffering—
And soul by soul and silently her shining bounds increase,
And her ways are ways of gentleness and all her paths are
     peace.

England, my England

W. E. HENLEY

WHAT have I done for you,
    England, my England?
What is there I would not do,
    England, my own?
With your glorious eyes austere,
As the Lord were walking near,
Whispering terrible things and dear
    As the Song on your bugles blown,
       England—
    Round the world on your bugles blown!

Where shall the watchful sun,
    England, my England,
Match the master-work you've done,
    England, my own?
When shall he rejoice agen
Such a breed of mighty men
As come forward, one to ten,
    To the Song on your bugles blown,
       England—
    Down the years on your bugles blown?

Ever the faith endures,
   England, my England:—
" Take and break us: we are yours,
   England, my own!
Life is good, and joy runs high
Between English earth and sky:
Death is death; but we shall die
   To the Song on your bugles blown,
     England—
   To the stars on your bugles blown! "

They call you proud and hard,
   England, my England:
You with worlds to watch and ward,
   England, my own!
You whose mail'd hand keeps the keys
Of such teeming destinies,
You could know nor dread nor ease
   Were the Song on your bugles blown,
     England,
   Round the Pit on your bugles blown!

Mother of Ships whose might,
   England, my England,
Is the fierce old Sea's delight,
   England, my own,
Chosen daughter of the Lord,
Spouse-in-Chief of the ancient Sword,
There's the menace of the Word
   In the Song on your bugles blown,
     England—
   Out of heaven on your bugles blown!

A Song of England

ALFRED NOYES

THERE is a song of England that none shall ever sing;
      So sweet it is and fleet it is
That none whose words are not as fleet as birds upon the
    wing,
        And regal as her mountains,
        And radiant as the fountains
Of rainbow-coloured sea-sprays that every wave can fling
Against the cliffs of England, the sturdy cliffs of England,
        Could more than seem to dream of it,
        Or catch one flying gleam of it,
Above the seas of England that never cease to sing.

There is a song of England that only lovers know;
      So rare it is and fair it is,
O, like a fairy rose it is upon a drift of snow,
        So cold and sweet and sunny,
        So full of hidden honey,
So like a flight of butterflies where rose and lily blow
Along the lanes of England, the leafy lanes of England;
        When flowers are at their vespers
        And full of little whispers,
The boys and girls of England shall sing it as they go.

There is a song of England that only love may sing,
      So sure it is and pure it is;
And seaward with the sea-mew it spreads a whiter wing,
        And with the sky-lark hovers
        Above the tryst of lovers,
Above the kiss and whisper that led the lovely Spring

G   M.V.

Through all the glades of England, the ferny glades of
 England,
   Until the way enwound her
   With sprays of may, and crowned her
With stars of frosty blossom in a merry morris-ring.

There is a song of England that haunts her hours of rest:
   The calm of it and balm of it
Are breathed from every hedgerow that blushes to the
 West:
   From the cottage doors that nightly
   Cast their welcome out so brightly
On the lanes where laughing children are lifted and
 caressed
By the tenderest hands in England, hard and blistered
 hands of England:
   And from the restful sighing
   Of the sleepers that are lying
With the arms of God around them on the night's
 contented breast.

There is a song of England that wanders on the wind;
   So sad it is and glad it is
That men who hear it madden and their eyes are wet
 and blind,
   For the lowlands and the highlands
   Of the unforgotten islands,
For the Islands of the Blessèd and the rest they cannot
 find
As they grope in dreams to England and the love they
 left in England;
   Little feet that danced to meet them
   And the lips that used to greet them,
And the watcher at the window in the home they left
 behind.

There is a song of England that thrills the beating blood
      With burning cries and yearning
Tides of hidden aspiration hardly known or understood;
       Aspirations of the creature
       Tow'rds the unity of Nature;
Sudden chivalries revealing whence the longing is
   renewed
In the men that live for England, live and love and die
   for England:
       By the light of their desire
       They shall blindly blunder higher,
To a wider, grander Kingdom and a deeper, nobler Good.

There is a song of England that only heaven can hear;
       So gloriously victorious,
It soars above the choral stars that sing the Golden Year;
       Till even the cloudy shadows
       That wander o'er her meadows
In silent purple harmonies declare His glory there,
Along the hills of England, the billowy hills of England;
       While heaven rolls and ranges
       Through all the myriad changes
That mirror God in music to the mortal eye and ear.

There is a song of England that none shall ever sing;
       So sweet it is and fleet it is
That none whose words are not as fleet as birds upon the wing,
       And regal as her mountains,
       And radiant as the fountains
Of rainbow-coloured sea-spray that every wave can fling
Against the cliffs of England, the sturdy cliffs of England,
       Could more than seem to dream of it,
       Or catch one flying gleam of it,
Above the seas of England that never cease to sing.

At Kew

ALFRED NOYES

Go down to Kew in lilac-time, in lilac-time, in lilac-time;
Go down to Kew in lilac-time (it isn't far from London!)
And you shall wander hand in hand with love in summer's
    wonderland;
Go down to Kew in lilac-time (it isn't far from London!)

The cherry-trees are seas of bloom and soft perfume and
    sweet perfume,
The cherry-trees are seas of bloom (and oh, so near to
    London!)
And there they say, when dawn is high and all the
    world's a blaze of sky,
The cuckoo, though he's very shy, will sing a song for
    London.

The nightingale is rather rare, and yet they say you'll
    hear him there,
At Kew, at Kew, in lilac-time (and oh, so near to
    London!)
The linnet and the throstle, too, and after dark the long
    halloo
And golden-eyed *tu-whit, tu-whoo*, of owls that ogle
    London.

For Noah hardly knew a bird of any kind that isn't
    heard
At Kew, at Kew, in lilac-time (and oh, so near to
    London!)

And when the rose begins to pout and all the chestnut
    spires are out
You'll hear the rest without a doubt, all chorusing for
    London:—

Come down to Kew in lilac-time, in lilac-time, in lilac-time;
Come down to Kew in lilac-time (it isn't far from London!)
And you shall wander hand in hand with love in summer's
    wonderland;
Come down to Kew in lilac-time (it isn't far from London!)

Lochinvar

SIR WALTER SCOTT

O, YOUNG Lochinvar is come out of the west,
Through all the wide Border his steed was the best,
And save his good broad-sword he weapons had none;
He rode all unarmed, and he rode all alone.
So faithful in love, and so dauntless in war,
There never was knight like the young Lochinvar.

He stayed not for brake, and he stopped not for stone,
He swam the Eske river where ford there was none;
But, ere he alighted at Netherby gate,
The bride had consented, the gallant came late:
For a laggard in love, and a dastard in war,
Was to wed the fair Ellen of brave Lochinvar.

So boldly he entered the Netherby hall,
Among bride's-men and kinsmen, and brothers and all:
Then spoke the bride's father, his hand on his sword
(For the poor craven bridegroom said never a word),
" O come ye in peace here, or come ye in war,
Or to dance at our bridal, young Lord Lochinvar? "

" I long wooed your daughter, my suit you denied;—
Love swells like the Solway, but ebbs like its tide—
And now I am come, with this lost love of mine,
To lead but one measure, drink one cup of wine.
There are maidens in Scotland more lovely by far,
That would gladly be bride to the young Lochinvar."

The bride kissed the goblet; the knight took it up,
He quaffed off the wine, and he threw down the cup,
She looked down to blush, and she looked up to sigh,
With a smile on her lips and a tear in her eye.
He took her soft hand, ere her mother could bar,—
" Now tread we a measure! " said young Lochinvar.

So stately his form, and so lovely her face,
That never a hall such a galliard did grace;
While her mother did fret, and her father did fume,
And the bridegroom stood dangling his bonnet and plume;
And the bride-maidens whispered, " 'Twere better by far
To have matched our fair cousin with young Lochinvar."

One touch to her hand, and one word in her ear,
When they reached the hall-door, and the charger stood
     near;
So light to the croupe the fair lady he swung,
So light to the saddle before her he sprung!
" She is won! we are gone, over bank, bush, and scaur;
They'll have fleet steeds that follow," quoth young
     Lochinvar.

There was mounting 'mong Graemes of the Netherby clan;
Forsters, Fenwicks, and Musgraves, they rode and they ran;
There was racing, and chasing, on Cannobie Lee,
But the lost bride of Netherby ne'er did they see.
So daring in love, and so dauntless in war,
Have ye e'er heard of gallant like young Lochinvar?

The Combat

SIR WALTER SCOTT

THE chief in silence strode before,
And reach'd that torrent's sounding shore,
Which, daughter of three mighty lakes,
From Vennachar in silver breaks,
Sweeps through the plain, and ceaseless mines
On Bochastle the mouldering lines,
Where Rome, the Empress of the world,
Of yore her eagle-wings unfurl'd.
And here his course the Chieftain staid,
Threw down his target and his plaid,
And to the Lowland warrior said—
" Bold Saxon! to his promise just,
Vich Alpine has discharged his trust.
This murderous Chief, this ruthless man,
This head of a rebellious clan,
Hath led thee safe through watch and ward,
Far past Clan-Alpine's outmost guard.
Now, man to man, and steel to steel,
A Chieftain's vengeance thou shalt feel.
See, here, all vantageless I stand,
Armed, like thyself, with single brand:
For this is Coilantogle ford,
And thou must keep thee with thy sword.
The Saxon paused: " I ne'er delayed,
When foeman bade me draw my blade;
Nay, more, brave Chief, I vowed thy death;
Yet sure thy fair and generous faith,
And my deep debt for life preserv'd,
A better meed have well deserved.
Can nought but blood our feud atone?
Are there no means? "   " No, Stranger, none:

And hear, to fire thy flagging zeal,—
The Saxon cause rests on thy steel;
For thus spoke Fate, by prophet bred,
Between the living and the dead:
' Who spills the foremost foeman's life,
His party conquers in the strife.' "—
" Then, by my word," the Saxon said,
" The riddle is already read.
Seek yonder brake beneath the cliff,—
There lies Red Murdoch, stark and stiff.
Thus Fate has solved her prophecy,
Then yield to Fate, and not to me.
To James, at Stirling, let us go,
When, if thou wilt be still his foe,
Or if the King shall not agree
To grant thee grace and favour free,
I plight mine honour, oath, and word,
That, to thy native strengths restored,
With each advantage shalt thou stand,
That aids thee now to guard thy land."

Dark lightning flashed from Roderick's eye—
" Soars thy presumption then so high,
Because a wretched kern ye slew,
Homage to name to Roderick Dhu?
He yields not, he, to man nor Fate!
Thou add'st but fuel to my hate:—
My clansman's blood demands revenge.
Not yet prepared?   By heaven, I change
My thought, and hold thy valour light
As that of some vain carpet knight,
Who ill deserved my courteous care,
And whose best boast is but to wear
A braid of his fair lady's hair."—

" I thank thee, Roderick, for the word;
It nerves my heart, it steels my sword;
For I have sworn this braid to stain
In the best blood that warms thy vein.
Now, truce, farewell! and, ruth, begone!—
Yet think not that by thee alone,
Proud Chief! can courtesy be shown;
Though not from copse, or heath, or cairn,
Start at my whistle clansmen stern,
Of this small horn one feeble blast
Would fearful odds against thee cast.
But fear not—doubt not—which thou wilt,
We try this quarrel hilt to hilt."—
Then each at once his falchion drew,
Each on the ground his scabbard threw,
Each look'd to sun, and stream, and plain,
As what they ne'er might see again;
Then foot, and point, and eye opposed,
In dubious strife they darkly closed.
Ill fared it then with Roderick Dhu,
That on the field his targe he threw,
Whose brazen studs and tough bull-hide
Had death so often dashed aside;
For, train'd abroad his arms to wield,
Fitz-James's blade was sword and shield.
He practised every pass and ward,
To thrust, to strike, to feint, to guard;
While less expert, though stronger far,
The Gael maintained unequal war.
Three times in closing strife they stood,
And thrice the Saxon blade drank blood;
No stinted draught, no scanty tide,
The gushing flood the tartans dyed.
Fierce Roderick felt the fatal drain,
And shower'd his blows like wintry rain;

G*

And, as firm rock, or castle roof,
Against the winter shower is proof,
The foe, invulnerable still,
Foil'd his wild rage by steady skill;
Till, at advantage ta'en, his brand
Forced Roderick's weapon from his hand,
And backward borne upon the lea,
Brought the proud Chieftain to his knee.

" Now, yield thee, or by Him who made
The world, thy heart's blood dyes my blade! "
—" Thy threats, thy mercy, I defy!
Let recreant yield who fears to die."
—Like adder darting from its coil,
Like wolf that dashes through the toil,
Like mountain-cat who guards her young,
Full at Fitz-James's throat he sprung;
Receiv'd, but recked not of a wound,
And lock'd his arms his foeman round.—
Now, gallant Saxon, hold thine own!
No maiden's hand is round thee thrown!
That desperate grasp thy frame might feel
Through bars of brass and triple steel!
They tug, they strain!   Down, down they go,
The Gael above, Fitz-James below.
The Chieftain's grip his throat compress'd,
His knee was planted on his breast;
His clotted locks he backward threw,
Across his brow his hand he drew,
From blood and mist to clear his sight,
Then gleam'd aloft his dagger bright!
—But hate and fury ill supplied
The stream of life's exhausted tide,
And all too late the advantage came,
To turn the odds of deadly game;

For, while the dagger gleam'd on high,
Reel'd soul and sense, reel'd brain and eye.
Down came the blow! but in the heath
The erring blade found bloodless sheath.
The struggling foe may now unclasp
The fainting Chief's relaxing grasp;
Unwounded from the dreadful close,
But breathless all, Fitz-James arose.

The Celestial Surgeon

ROBERT LOUIS STEVENSON

IF I have faltered more or less
In my great task of happiness;
If I have moved among my race
And shown no glorious morning face;
If beams from happy human eyes
Have moved me not; if morning skies,
Books, and my food, and summer rain
Knocked on my sullen heart in vain:—
Lord, thy most pointed pleasure take
And stab my spirit broad awake;
Or, Lord, if too obdurate I,
Choose thou, before that spirit die,
A piercing pain, a killing sin,
And to my dead heart run them in!

O my Luve's like a Red, Red Rose

ROBERT BURNS

O MY Luve's like a red, red rose
    That's newly sprung in June:
O my Luve's like the melodie
    That's sweetly play'd in tune.

As fair art thou, my bonnie lass,
  So deep in luve am I:
And I will luve thee still, my dear,
  Till a' the seas gang dry:

Till a' the seas gang dry, my dear,
  And the rocks melt wi' the sun;
I will luve thee still, my dear,
  While the sands o' life shall run.

And fare thee weel, my only Luve!
  And fare thee weel a while!
And I will come again, my Luve,
  Tho' it were ten thousand mile.

Haste thee, Nymph

JOHN MILTON

HASTE thee, Nymph, and bring with thee
Jest, and youthful Jollity,
Quips and Cranks and wanton Wiles,
Nods and Becks and wreathéd Smiles,
Such as hang on Hebe's cheek,
And love to live in dimple sleek;
Sport that wrinkled Care derides,
And Laughter holding both his sides.
Come, and trip it, as you go,
On the light fantastic toe;
And in thy right hand lead with thee
The mountain-nymph, sweet Liberty;
And, if I give thee honour due,
Mirth, admit me of thy crew,
To live with her, and live with thee,
In unreprovéd pleasures free;

To hear the lark begin his flight,
And, singing, startle the dull night,
From his watch-tower in the skies,
Till the dappled dawn doth rise;
Then to come, in spite of sorrow,
And at my window bid good-morrow,
Through the sweet-brier or the vine,
Or the twisted eglantine;
While the cock, with lively din,
Scatters the rear of darkness thin;
And to the stack, or the barn-door,
Stoutly struts his dames before:
Oft list'ning how the hounds and horn
Cheerly rouse the slumb'ring morn,
From the side of some hoar hill,
Through the high wood echoing shrill:
Sometime walking, not unseen,
By hedgerow elms, on hillocks green,
Right against the eastern gate,
Where the great Sun begins his state,
Robed in flames and amber light,
The clouds in thousand liveries dight;
While the ploughman, near at hand,
Whistles o'er the furrow'd land,
And the milkmaid singeth blithe,
And the mower whets his scythe,
And every shepherd tells his tale
Under the hawthorn in the dale.
Straight mine eye hath caught new pleasures,
Whilst the landskip round it measures:
Russet lawns, and fallows grey,
Where the nibbling flocks do stray;
Mountains on whose barren breast
The labouring clouds do often rest;

Meadows trim with daisies pied;
Shallow brooks, and rivers wide;
Towers and battlements it sees
Bosomed high in tufted trees,
Where perhaps some beauty lies,
The cynosure of neighbouring eyes.
Hard by a cottage chimney smokes
From betwixt two agéd oaks,
Where Corydon and Thyrsis met
Are at their savoury dinner set
Of herbs and other country messes,
Which the neat-handed Phyllis dresses;
And then in haste her bower she leaves,
With Thestylis to bind the sheaves;
Or, if the earlier season lead,
To the tanned haycock in the mead,
Sometimes, with secure delight,
The upland hamlets will invite,
When the merry bells ring round,
And the jocund rebecks sound
To many a youth and many a maid
Dancing in the chequer'd shade,
And young and old come forth to play
On a sunshine holiday,
Till the livelong daylight fail,
Then to the spicy nut-brown ale,
With stories told of many a feat,
How Faery Mab the junkets eat,
She was pinch'd and pull'd, she said:
And he, by Friar's lantern led,
Tells how the drudging goblin sweat
To earn his cream-bowl duly set,
When in one night, ere glimpse of morn,
His shadowy flail hath thresh'd the corn

That ten day-labourers could not end;
Then lies him down, the lubber fiend,
And, stretch'd out all the chimney's length,
Basks at the fire his hairy strength;
And crop-full out of doors he flings,
Ere the first cock his matin rings.
Thus done the tales, to bed they creep,
By whispering winds soon lull'd asleep.
Tower'd cities please us then,
And the busy hum of men,
Where throngs of knights and barons bold,
In weeds of peace, high triumphs hold,
With store of ladies, whose bright eyes
Rain influence, and judge the prize
Of wit or arms, while both contend
To win her grace whom all commend.
There let Hymen oft appear
In saffron robe, with taper clear,
And pomp, and feast, and revelry,
With mask, and antique pageantry;
Such sights as youthful poets dream
On summer eves by haunted stream.
Then to the well-trod stage anon,
If Jonson's learned sock be on,
Or sweetest Shakespeare, Fancy's child,
Warble his native wood-notes wild.

And ever, against eating cares,
Lap me in soft Lydian airs,
Married to immortal verse,
Such as the meeting soul may pierce
In notes, with many a winding bout
Of linkéd sweetness long drawn out,
With wanton heed, and giddy cunning,
The melting voice through mazes running,

Untwisting all the chains that tie
The hidden soul of harmony;
That Orpheus' self may heave his head
From golden slumber on a bed
Of heap'd Elysian flowers, and hear
Such strains as would have won the ear
Of Pluto, to have quite set free
His half-regain'd Eurydice.

These delights, if thou canst give,
Mirth with thee, I mean to live.

A Legend of Bregenz

ADELAIDE PROCTER

GIRT round with rugged mountains
  The fair Lake Constance lies,
In her blue heart reflected
  Shine back the starry skies,
And, watching each white cloudlet
  Float silently and slow,
You think a piece of Heaven
  Lies on our earth below.

Midnight is there; and silence
  Enthroned in heaven, looks down
Upon her own calm mirror,
  Upon a sleeping town;
For Bregenz, that quaint city
  Upon the Tyrol shore,
Has stood above Lake Constance
  A thousand years and more.

Her battlements and towers
   From off their rocky steep
Have cast their trembling shadow
   For ages on the deep.
Mountain and lake and valley
   A sacred legend know—
Of how the town was saved one night
   Three hundred years ago.

Far from her home and kindred
   A Tyrol maid had fled,
To serve in the Swiss valleys,
   And toil for daily bread;
And every year that fleeted
   So silently and fast,
Seemed to bear farther from her
   The memory of the Past.

She served kind, gentle masters,
   Nor asked for rest or change.
Her friends seemed no more new ones,
   Their speech seemed no more strange;
And when she led her cattle
   To pasture every day,
She ceased to look and wonder
   On which side Bregenz lay.

She spoke no more of Bregenz
   With longing and with tears,
Her Tyrol home seemed faded
   In a deep mist of years.
She heeded not the rumours
   Of Austrian war and strife.
Each day she rose, contented,
   To the calm toils of life.

Yet when her master's children
   Would clustering round her stand,
She sang them ancient ballads
   Of her own native land;
And when at morn and evening
   She knelt before God's throne,
The accents of her childhood
   Rose to her lips alone.

And so she dwelt—the valley
   More peaceful year by year—
When suddenly strange portents
   Of some great deed seemed near.
The golden corn was bending
   Upon its fragile stalk,
While farmers, heedless of their fields,
   Paced up and·down in talk.

The men seemed stern and altered,
   With looks cast on the ground:
With anxious faces, one by one,
   The women gathered round:
All talk of flax, or spinning,
   Or work, was put away:
The very children seemed afraid
   To go alone to play.

One day, out in the meadow
   With strangers from the town—
Some secret plan discussing—
   The men walked up and down.
Yet now and then seemed watching
   A strange uncertain gleam
That looked like lances 'mid the trees
   That stood below the stream.

At eve they all assembled;
   Then care and doubt were fled;
With jovial laugh they feasted—
   The board was nobly spread.
The elder of the village
   Rose up, his glass in hand,
And cried: " We drink the downfall
   Of an accursèd land!

" The night is growing darker;
   Ere one more day is flown,
Bregenz, our foemen's stronghold,
   Bregenz shall be our own! "
The women shrank in terror
   (Yet pride, too, had her part).
But one poor Tyrol maiden
   Felt death within her heart.

Before her stood fair Bregenz,
   Once more her towers arose.
What were the friends beside her?
   Only her country's foes!
The faces of her kinsfolk,
   The days of childhood flown,
The echoes of her mountains
   Reclaimed her as their own!

Nothing she heard around her
   (Though shouts rang forth again).
Gone were the green Swiss valleys,
   The pasture and the plain.
Before her eyes one vision,
   And in her heart one cry
That said: " Go forth! Save Bregenz!
   And then—if need be—die! "

With trembling haste, and breathless,
　With noiseless step she sped.
Horses and weary cattle
　Were standing in the shed.
She loosed the strong white charger,
　That fed from out her hand;
She mounted, and she turned his head
　Towards her native land.

Out—out into the darkness,
　Faster and still more fast—
The smooth grass flies behind her—
　The chestnut wood is passed.
She looks up; clouds are heavy—
　Why is her steed so slow?
Scarcely the wind beside them
　Can pass them as they go.

" Faster! " she cries.　" Oh, faster! "
　Eleven the church bells chime.
" Oh God," she cries, " help Bregenz!
　And bring me there in time! "
But louder than bells ringing,
　Or lowing of the kine,
Grows nearer in the midnight
　The rushing of the Rhine.

Shall not the roaring waters
　Their headlong gallop check?
The steed draws back in terror;
　She leans upon his neck
To watch the flowing darkness.
　The bank is high and steep.
One pause—he staggers forward
　And plunges in the deep.

She strives to pierce the blackness,
   And looser throws the rein—
Her steed must breast the waters
   That dash above his mane.
How gallantly, how nobly,
   He struggles through the foam—
And see!   In the far distance
   Shine out the lights of home!

Up the steep banks he bears her,
   And now they rush again
Towards the heights of Bregenz,
   That tower above the plain.
They reach the gate of Bregenz
   Just as the midnight rings,
And out come serf and soldier
   To meet the news she brings.

Bregenz is saved!   Ere daylight
   Her battlements are manned,
Defiance greets the army
   That marches on the land.
And if to deeds heroic
   Should endless fame be paid,
Bregenz does well to honour
   The noble Tyrol maid.

Three hundred years are vanished,
   And yet upon the hill
An old stone gateway rises
   To do her honour still:
And there, when Bregenz women
   Sit spinning in the shade,
They see in quaint old carving
   The Charger and the Maid.

And when, to guard old Bregenz,
   By gateway, street and tower,
The warder paces all night long,
   And calls each passing hour—
" Nine! " " Ten! " " Eleven! " he cries aloud,
   And then (Oh, crown of Fame!)
When midnight pauses in the skies,
   He calls the maiden's name!

The Song of the Western Men

R. S. HAWKER

A GOOD sword and a trusty hand!
   A merry heart and true!
King James's men shall understand
   What Cornish lads can do.

And have they fixed the where and when?
   And shall Trelawney die?
Then twenty thousand Cornish men
   Will know the reason why!

Out spake their captain brave and bold,
   A merry wight was he:
" If London Tower were Michael's Hold,
   We'll set Trelawney free!

" We'll cross the Tamar, land to land,
   The Severn is no stay,
With ' one and all,' and hand in hand,
   And who shall bid us nay?

" And when we come to London Wall,
   A pleasant sight to view,
Come forth! come forth! ye cowards all,
   Here's men as good as you.

" Trelawney he's in keep and hold,
   Trelawney he may die;
But twenty thousand Cornish bold
   Will know the reason why! "

The Skylark

PERCY BYSSHE SHELLEY

HAIL to thee, blithe spirit—
   Bird thou never wert—
That from heaven, or near it,
   Pourest thy full heart
In profuse strains of unpremeditated art!

   Higher still and higher
      From the earth thou springest
   Like a cloud of fire;
      The blue deep thou wingest,
And singing still dost soar, and soaring ever singest.

   In the golden lightning
      Of the sunken sun,
   O'er which clouds are bright'ning,
      Thou dost float and run;
Like an unbodied joy whose race is just begun.

The pale purple even
    Melts around thy flight;
Like a star of heaven,
    In the broad day-light
Thou art unseen, but yet I hear thy shrill delight—

Keen as are the arrows
    Of that silver sphere,
Whose intense lamp narrows
    In the white dawn clear,
Until we hardly see, we feel that it is there.

All the earth and air
    With thy voice is loud,
As, when night is bare,
    From one lonely cloud
The moon rains out her beams, and heaven is overflowed.

What thou art we know not;
    What is most like thee?
From rainbow clouds there flow not
    Drops so bright to see,
As from thy presence showers a rain of melody.

Like a poet hidden
    In the light of thought,
Singing hymns unbidden,
    Till the world is wrought,
To sympathy with hopes and fears it heeded not:

Like a high-born maiden
    In a palace tower,
Soothing her love-laden
    Soul in secret hour
With music sweet as love, which overflows her bower:

Like a glow-worm golden
      In a dell of dew,
Scattering unbeholden
      Its aërial hue
Among the flowers and grass, which screen it from the view:

Like a rose embowered
      In its own green leaves,
By warm winds deflowered,
      Till the scent it gives
Makes faint with too much sweet these heavy-wingéd
      thieves:

Sound of vernal showers
      On the twinkling grass,
Rain-awakened flowers,
      All that ever was
Joyous, and clear, and fresh, thy music doth surpass:

Teach us, sprite or bird,
      What sweet thoughts are thine:
I have never heard
      Praise of love or wine
That panted forth a flood of rapture so divine.

Chorus Hymenæal,
      Or triumphal chaunt,
Matched with thine would be all
      But an empty vaunt,
A thing wherein we feel there is some hidden want.

What objects are the fountains
      Of thy happy strain?
What fields, or waves, or mountains?
      What shapes of sky or plain?
What love of thine own kind? what ignorance of pain?

With thy clear keen joyance
    Languor cannot be:
Shadow of annoyance
    Never came near thee:
Thou lovest; but ne'er knew love's sad satiety.

Waking or asleep,
    Thou of death must deem
Things more true and deep
    Than we mortals dream,
Or how could thy notes flow in such a crystal stream?

We look before and after,
    And pine for what is not:
Our sincerest laughter
    With some pain is fraught;
Our sweetest songs are those that tell of saddest thought.

Yet if we could scorn
    Hate, and pride, and fear;
If we were things born
    Not to shed a tear,
I know not how thy joy we ever should come near.

Better than all measures
    Of delightful sound,
Better than all treasures
    That in books are found,
Thy skill to poet were, thou scorner of the ground!

Teach me half the gladness
    That thy brain must know,
Such harmonious madness
    From my lips would flow,
The world should listen then as I am listening now.

The Garden

ANDREW MARVELL

How vainly men themselves amaze
To win the palm, the oak, or bays,
And their incessant labours see
Crown'd from some single herb, or tree,
Whose short and narrow-vergéd shade
Does prudently their toils upbraid;
While all the flowers and trees do close,
To weave the garlands of repose.

  Fair Quiet, have I found thee here,
And Innocence, thy sister dear?
Mistaken long, I sought you then
In busy companies of men.
Your sacred plants, if here below,
Only among the plants will grow;
Society is all but rude
To this delicious solitude.

  No white nor red was ever seen
So amorous as this lovely green.
Fond lovers, cruel as their flame,
Cut in these trees their mistress' name.
Little, alas, they know or heed,
How far these beauties her exceed!
Fair trees! where'er your barks I wound,
No name shall but your own be found.

  When we have run our passion's heat,
Love hither makes his best retreat.
The gods, who mortal beauty chase,
Still in a tree did end their race.
Apollo hunted Daphne so,
Only that she might laurel grow:

And Pan did after Syrinx speed,
Not as a nymph, but for a reed.

What wondrous life in this I lead!
Ripe apples drop about my head;
The luscious clusters of the vine
Upon my mouth do crush their wine.
The nectarine, and curious peach,
Into my hands themselves do reach.
Stumbling on melons, as I pass,
Ensnared with flowers, I fall on grass.

Meanwhile the mind, from pleasure less,
Withdraws into its happiness;
The mind, that ocean where each kind
Does straight its own resemblance find;
Yet it creates, transcending these,
Far other worlds, and other seas;
Annihilating all that's made
To a green thought in a green shade.

Here at the fountain's sliding foot,
Or at some fruit-tree's mossy root,
Casting the body's vest aside,
My soul into the boughs does glide:
There, like a bird, it sits and sings,
Then whets, and claps its silver wings;
And, till prepar'd for longer flight,
Waves its plumes the various light.

Such was that happy garden-state,
While man there walked without a mate;
After a place so pure and sweet,
What other help could yet be meet!
But 'twas beyond a mortal's share
To wander solitary there:
Two paradises are in one,
To live in paradise alone.

How well the skilful gardener drew
Of flowers, and herbs, this dial new:
Where, from above, the milder sun
Does through a fragrant zodiac run:
And, as it works, the industrious bee
Computes his time as well as we!
How could such sweet and wholesome hours
Be reckoned but with herbs and flowers?

The Private of the Buffs

SIR F. H. DOYLE

Last night, among his fellow roughs,
    He jested, quaffed, and swore;
A drunken private of the Buffs,
    Who never looked before.
To-day, beneath the foeman's frown,
    He stands in Elgin's place,
Ambassador from Britain's crown,
    And type of all her race.

Poor, reckless, rude, low-born, untaught,
    Bewildered, and alone,
A heart, with English instinct fraught,
    He yet can call his own.
Ay, tear his body limb from limb,
    Bring cord, or axe, or flame;
He only knows, that not through *him*
    Shall England come to shame.

Far Kentish hop-fields round him seem'd,
    Like dreams, to come and go;
Bright leagues of cherry-blossom gleam'd,
    One sheet of living snow;

The smoke, above his father's door,
  In gray soft eddyings hung:
Must he then watch it rise no more,
  Doom'd by himself, so young?

Yes, honour calls!—with strength like steel
  He put the vision by.
Let dusky Indians whine and kneel;
  An English lad must die.
And thus, with eyes that would not shrink,
  With knee to man unbent,
Unfaltering on its dreadful brink,
  To his red grave he went.

Vain, mightiest fleets, of iron framed;
  Vain, those all-shattering guns;
Unless proud England keep, untamed,
  The strong heart of her sons.
So, let his name through Europe ring—
  A man of mean estate,
Who died, as firm as Sparta's king,
  Because his soul was great.

The South Country

HILAIRE BELLOC

WHEN I am living in the Midlands
  That are sodden and unkind,
I light my lamp in the evening:
  My work is left behind;
And the great hills of the South Country
  Come back into my mind.

The great hills of the South Country
 They stand along the sea;
And it's there walking in the high woods
 That I could wish to be,
And the men that were boys when I was a boy
 Walking along with me.

The men that live in North England
 I saw them for a day:
Their hearts are set upon the waste fells,
 Their skies are fast and grey;
From their castle-walls a man may see
 The mountains far away.

The men that live in West England
 They see the Severn strong,
A-rolling on rough water brown
 Light aspen leaves along.
They have the secret of the Rocks,
 And the oldest kind of song.

But the men that live in the South Country
 Are the kindest and most wise,
They get their laughter from the loud surf,
 And the faith in their happy eyes
Comes surely from our Sister the Spring
 When over the sea she flies;
The violets suddenly bloom at her feet,
 She blesses us with surprise.

I never get between the pines
 But I smell the Sussex air;
Nor I never come on a belt of sand
 But my home is there.
And along the sky the line of the Downs
 So noble and so bare.

A lost thing could I never find,
  Nor a broken thing mend:
And I fear I shall be all alone
  When I get towards the end.
Who will there be to comfort me
  Or who will be my friend?

I will gather and carefully make my friends
  Of the men of the Sussex Weald,
They watch the stars from silent folds,
  They stiffly plough the field.
By them and the God of the South Country
  My poor soul shall be heal'd.

If I ever become a rich man,
  Or if ever I grow to be old,
I will build a house with deep thatch
  To shelter me from the cold,
And there shall the Sussex songs be sung
  And the story of Sussex told.

I will hold my house in the high wood
  Within a walk of the sea,
And the men that were boys when I was a boy
  Shall sit and drink with me.

A Ballade to Queen Elizabeth
of the Spanish Armada

AUSTIN DOBSON

KING PHILIP had vaunted his claims;
  He had sworn for a year he would sack us;
With an army of heathenish names
  He was coming to fagot and stack us;

Like the thieves of the sea he would track us,
And shatter our ships on the main;
  But we had bold Neptune to back us—
And where are the galleons of Spain?

His carackes were christened of dames
  To the kirtles whereof he would tack us;
With his saints and his gilded stern-frames
  He had thought like an egg-shell to crack us;
  Now Howard may get to his Flaccus,
And Drake to his Devon again,
  And Hawkins bowl rubbers to Bacchus—
For where are the galleons of Spain?

Let his Majesty hang to St. James
  The axe that he whetted to hack us;
He must play at some lustier games
  Or at sea he can hope to out-thwack us;
  To his mines of Peru he would pack us
To tug at his bullet and chain;
  Alas! that his greatness should lack us!—
But where are the galleons of Spain?

ENVOY

Gloriana!—the Don may attack us
Whenever his stomach be fain;
  He must reach us before he can rack us,
And where are the galleons of Spain?

The Oxen

THOMAS HARDY

CHRISTMAS EVE, and twelve of the clock.
   " Now they are all on their knees,"
An elder said as we sat in a flock
   By the embers in hearthside ease.

We pictured the meek mild creatures where
   They dwelt in their strawy pen,
Nor did it occur to one of us there
   To doubt they were kneeling then.

So fair a fancy few would weave
   In these years!   Yet, I feel,
If someone said on Christmas Eve,
   " Come; see the oxen kneel

" In the lonely barton by yonder coomb
   Our childhood used to know,"
I should go with him in the gloom.
   Hoping it might be so.

The Donkey

G. K. CHESTERTON

WHEN fishes flew and forests walked,
   And figs grew upon thorn,
Some moments when the moon was blood,
   Then surely I was born;

With monstrous head and sickening cry
  And ears like errant wings,
The devil's walking parody
  On all four-footed things.

The tattered outlaw of the earth,
  Of ancient crooked will;
Starve, scourge, deride me: I am dumb,
  I keep my secret still.

Fools! For I also had my hour;
  One far fierce hour and sweet:
There was a shout about my ears,
  And palms before my feet.

Sea Fever

JOHN MASEFIELD

I MUST go down to the seas again, to the lonely sea and
    the sky,
And all I ask is a tall ship, and a star to steer her by;
And the wheel's kick and the wind's song and the white
    sails shaking,
And the grey mist on the sea's face, and a grey dawn
    breaking.

I must go down to the seas again, for the call of the
    running tide
Is a wild call and a clear call that may not be denied;
And all I ask is a windy day with the white clouds flying,
And the flung spray and the blown spume, and the sea-
    gulls crying.

I must go down to the seas again, to the vagrant gypsy
    life,
To the gull's way and the whale's way where the wind's
    like a whetted knife;
And all I ask is a merry yarn from a laughing fellow
    rover,
And quiet sleep and a sweet dream when the long trick's
    over.

To Celia

BEN JONSON

DRINK to me only with thine eyes,
    And I will pledge with mine;
Or leave a kiss but in the cup
    And I'll not look for wine.
The thirst that from the soul doth rise
    Doth ask a drink divine;
But might I of Jove's nectar sup,
    I would not change for thine.

I sent thee late a rosy wreath,
    Not so much honouring thee
As giving it a hope that there
    It could not wither'd be;
But thou thereon didst only breathe,
    And sent'st it back to me;
Since when it grows, and smells, I swear,
    Not of itself but thee.

Widdecombe Fair

ANONYMOUS

" TOM PEARSE, Tom Pearse, lend me your grey mare,"
   All along, down along, out along, lee;
" For I want for to go to Widdecombe Fair,
   Wi' Bill Brewer, Jan Stewer, Peter Gurney, Peter Davy,
    Dan'l Whiddon, Harry Hawk,
   Old Uncle Tom Cobley and all."
       Old Uncle Tom Cobley and all.

" And when shall I see again my grey mare? "
   All along, down along, out along, lee;
" By Friday soon, or Saturday noon,
   Wi' Bill Brewer, Jan Stewer, Peter Gurney, Peter Davy,
    Dan'l Whiddon, Harry Hawk,
   Old Uncle Tom Cobley and all."
       Old Uncle Tom Cobley and all.

Then Friday came and Saturday noon,
   All along, down along, out along, lee;
But Tom Pearse's old mare hath not trotted home,
   Wi' Bill Brewer, Jan Stewer, Peter Gurney, Peter Davy,
    Dan'l Whiddon, Harry Hawk,
   Old Uncle Tom Cobley and all,
       Old Uncle Tom Cobley and all.

So Tom Pearse he got up to the top o' the hill,
   All along, down along, out along, lee;
And he seed his old mare down a-making her will,
   Wi' Bill Brewer, Jan Stewer, Peter Gurney, Peter Davy,
    Dan'l Whiddon, Harry Hawk,
   Old Uncle Tom Cobley and all,
       Old Uncle Tom Cobley and all.

So Tom Pearse's old mare took her sick and her died,
 All along, down along, out along, lee;
And Tom he sat down on a stone and he cried,
  Wi' Bill Brewer, Jan Stewer, Peter Gurney, Peter Davy,
   Dan'l Whiddon, Harry Hawk,
  Old Uncle Tom Cobley and all,
    Old Uncle Tom Cobley and all.

When the wind whistles cold on the moor of a night,
 All along, down along, out along, lee,
Tom Pearse's old mare doth appear, gashly white,
  Wi' Bill Brewer, Jan Stewer, Peter Gurney, Peter Davy,
   Dan'l Whiddon, Harry Hawk,
  Old Uncle Tom Cobley and all,
    Old Uncle Tom Cobley and all.

And all the long night he heard skirling and groans,
 All along, down along, out along, lee,
From Tom Pearse's old mare in her rattling bones,
  And from Bill Brewer, Jan Stewer, Peter Gurney, Peter
   Davy, Dan'l Whiddon, Harry Hawk,
  Old Uncle Tom Cobley and all,
    Old Uncle Tom Cobley and all.

Under the Greenwood Tree

WILLIAM SHAKESPEARE

UNDER the greenwood tree
Who loves to lie with me,
And tune his merry note
Unto the sweet bird's throat—
Come hither, come hither, come hither!
  Here shall he see
  No enemy
But winter and rough weather.

Who doth ambition shun
And loves to live i' the sun,
Seeking the food he eats
And pleased with what he gets—
Come hither, come hither, come hither!
Here shall he see
No enemy
But winter and rough weather.

As You Like It.

Come unto these Yellow Sands

WILLIAM SHAKESPEARE

Come unto these yellow sands,
And then take hands;
Curtsied when you have, and kiss'd,—
The wild waves whist,—

Foot it featly here and there;
And, sweet sprites, the burden bear.
Hark, hark!
The watch-dogs bark:
Hark, hark!   I hear
The strain of strutting Chanticleer.

The Tempest.

O Mistress Mine

WILLIAM SHAKESPEARE

O Mistress mine, where are you roaming?
O stay and hear! your true-love's coming,
That can sing both high and low;

Trip no further, pretty sweeting,
Journeys end in lovers meeting—
　　Every wise man's son doth know.

What is love? 'tis not hereafter;
Present mirth hath present laughter;
　　What's to come is still unsure:
In delay there lies no plenty,—
Then come kiss me, Sweet-and-twenty,
　　Youth's a stuff will not endure.

Twelfth Night.

Where the Bee sucks

WILLIAM SHAKESPEARE

WHERE the bee sucks, there suck I;
In a cowslip's bell I lie;
There I couch when owls do cry.
On the bat's back I do fly
After summer merrily.
Merrily, merrily shall I live now
Under the blossom that hangs on the bough.

The Tempest.

Blow, blow, thou Winter Wind

WILLIAM SHAKESPEARE

BLOW, blow, thou winter wind,
Thou art not so unkind
　　As man's ingratitude;
Thy tooth is not so keen,
Because thou art not seen,
　　Although thy breath be rude.

Heigh ho! sing, heigh ho! unto the green holly:
Most friendship is feigning, most loving mere folly:
      Then heigh ho, the holly!
      This life is most jolly.

      Freeze, freeze, thou bitter sky,
      That dost not bite so nigh
        As benefits forgot:
      Though thou the waters warp,
      Thy sting is not so sharp
        As friend remember'd not.
Heigh ho! sing, heigh ho! unto the green holly:
Most friendship is feigning, most loving mere folly:
      Then heigh ho, the holly!
      This life is most jolly.

As You Like It.

It was a Lover and his Lass

WILLIAM SHAKESPEARE

It was a lover and his lass,
  With a hey, and a ho, and a hey nonino,
That o'er the green cornfield did pass
  In the spring time, the only pretty ring time,
When birds do sing, hey ding a ding, ding;
  Sweet lovers love the spring.

Between the acres of the rye,
  With a hey, and a ho, and a hey nonino,
These pretty country folks would lie,
  In the spring time, the only pretty ring time,
When birds do sing, hey ding a ding, ding;
  Sweet lovers love the spring.

H*

This carol they began that hour,
  With a hey, and a ho, and a hey **nonino,**
How that life was but a flower
  In the spring time, the only pretty ring time,
When birds do sing, hey ding a ding, ding;
  Sweet lovers love the spring.

And therefore take the present time,
  With a hey, and a ho, and a hey nonino,
For love is crownéd with the prime
  In the spring time, the only pretty ring time,
When birds do sing, hey ding a ding, ding;
  Sweet lovers love the spring.

As You Like It.

Hark! Hark! the Lark

WILLIAM SHAKESPEARE

HARK! hark! the lark at Heaven's gate sings,
  And Phoebus 'gins arise,
His steeds to water at those springs
  On chaliced flowers that lies;
And winking Mary-buds begin
  To ope their golden eyes:
With everything that pretty bin,
  My lady sweet, arise!
    Arise, arise!

Cymbeline.

Rule, Britannia

JAMES THOMSON

WHEN Britain first at Heaven's command
   Arose from out the azure main,
This was the charter of her land,
   And guardian angels sang the strain:
Rule, Britannia! rule the waves!
    Britons never will be slaves.

The nations not so blest as thee
   Must in their turn to tyrants fall,
Whilst thou shalt flourish great and free,
   The dread and envy of them all.

Still more majestic shalt thou rise,
   More dreadful from each foreign stroke;
As the loud blast that tears the skies
   Serves but to root thy native oak.

Thee haughty tyrants ne'er shall tame;
   All their attempts to bend thee down
Will but arouse thy generous flame,
   And work their woe and thy renown.

To thee belongs the rural reign;
   Thy cities shall with commerce shine;
All thine shall be the subject main,
   And every shore it circles thine!

The Muses, still with Freedom found,
   Shall to thy happy coast repair;
Blest Isle, with matchless beauty crowned
   And manly hearts to guard the fair.
Rule, Britannia! rule the waves!
    Britons never will be slaves.

God save the Queen

ANONYMOUS

GOD save our gracious Queen,
Long live our noble Queen,
   God save the Queen.
Send her victorious,
Happy and glorious,
Long to reign over us,
   God save the Queen.

O Lord our God arise,
Scatter her enemies,
   And make them fall;
Confound their politics,
Frustrate their knavish tricks,
On Thee our hopes we fix,
   God save us all.

Thy choicest gifts in store,
On her be pleased to pour,
   Long may she reign.
May she defend our laws,
And ever give us cause,
To sing with heart and voice
   God save the Queen.

Biographical Notes

Addison, Joseph (1672-1719). Son of the Dean of Lichfield and born near Amesbury, Wilts. Educated at Charterhouse and Oxford. From the first he combined literature with politics, and after the production of his poem on the Battle of Blenheim, *The Campaign*, he was appointed Commissioner of Appeals, and, later, Under-Secretary of State. A subsequent appointment made him Chief Secretary for Ireland and Keeper of the Records of that country. In 1709 he became associated with Sir Richard Steele in the production of a journal named *The Tatler*, in which his essays attained great popularity. He afterwards founded with Steele two other papers, *The Spectator* and *The Guardian*, in which some of his most famous works appeared. In 1716 he married the Dowager Countess of Warwick and retired to The Manor House, at Sands End, Fulham, then a country hamlet ; the marriage, however, proved unhappy. Addison died at Holland House, Kensington.

Alexander, Mrs. C. F. (1818-1895). Daughter of Major Humphreys of Waterford, Ireland, where she was born. She married the Rev. W. Alexander, who was afterwards appointed Bishop of Derry and Archbishop of Armagh, and who also wrote several books of poetry. Mrs. Alexander's *Hymns for Little Children* enjoyed great popularity and went into many editions. She is specially remembered by her hymns, two of which— " There is a green hill far away " and " The roseate hues of early dawn "—are known the world over.

Allingham, William (1824-1889). Son of a banker and born at Ballyshannon, Ireland. He entered the Customs Service and came to London, where he combined literary work with his professional duties. Allingham contributed to *Leigh Hunt's Journal*, and produced his *Day and Night Songs* in 1854. In 1870 he retired from the Civil Service and became sub-editor of

Fraser's Magazine, under J. A. Froude, whom he subsequently succeeded as editor.

Belloc, Hilaire (1870-1953). Born in France, son of a French barrister. Educated at the Oratory School, Edgbaston. On leaving school he served in the French Army, returning later to Balliol College, Oxford. For some years he was M.P. for Salford. His literary output has been extremely varied. Among his best-known works may be mentioned the following : *The Bad Child's Book of Beasts*, *The Path to Rome*, *The Four Men*, his studies of Robespierre and Danton, his volumes of essays *On Something*, *On Nothing*, etc., his writings on travel, such as *Hills and the Sea*, and the striking poems collected in his *Verses and Sonnets*.

Blake, William (1757-1827). Born in London, the son of a hosier. He was apprenticed to an engraver, and afterwards studied at the Royal Academy Schools. Subsequently he set up as an independent engraver, and also ran a print-shop in conjunction with his brother. In 1782 he married Catherine Boucher, who, though unable to read or write, was educated by her husband, and became his bookbinder when he issued his *Songs of Innocence*, which he also illustrated. This was followed by *The Book of Thel*, his first mystical work, and *Songs of Experience*, among many other similar volumes, and his magnificent illustrations to the *Book of Job*. Blake was a man of great natural, if somewhat undisciplined, genius, and one biographer sums him up very accurately in the words : " A truly loving soul, Blake was neglected and misunderstood by the world, but appreciated by a select few ; he led a cheerful and contented life of poverty, illumined by vision."

Bridges, Robert (1844-1930). Born in the Isle of Thanet and educated at Eton and Corpus Christi College, Oxford. He studied at St. Bartholomew's Hospital, and became Casualty Physician there, and Assistant Physician at the Children's Hospital, Great Ormond Street, and at the Great Northern Hospital. He retired from medical work in 1882 and devoted himself to literature, and in 1913 was appointed Poet Laureate. His chief poetical works include the lyrics in his *Shorter Poems* and *New Verse*, his great *Testament of Beauty*, and several dramas on classical themes. His prose writings deal chiefly with subjects connected with poetry.

Browning, Robert (1812-1889). Born at Camberwell, the son of an official in the Bank of England. Browning was educated privately, and published his first work, *Pauline*, when he was twenty-one. Later he visited Italy, where much of his future life was destined to be spent, for after his marriage to Elizabeth Barrett, the poetess, in 1846, they settled in Florence until the latter's death in 1861. Browning was a profound thinker, and many of his poems at first seemed obscure and appealed to a somewhat narrow circle, but later he became more widely appreciated and studied. His best-known longer works include *Christmas Eve and Easter Day*, *Pippa Passes*, and *The Ring and the Book*, the last being, perhaps, his greatest work. To a large circle of younger readers he is best known by his shorter poems, such as *The Pied Piper of Hamelin* and *How they brought the good news from Ghent to Aix*. After his wife's death Browning lived mainly in London, though he died in Venice. He was buried in Westminster Abbey.

Burns, Robert (1759-1796). Son of a small farmer in Ayrshire. The poet's early life was spent on the farm, in adverse conditions, but in 1786, through the help of Dr. Thomas Blacklock, Burns published his first book of poems. This led to his visiting Edinburgh, where he was well received in literary circles. Eventually he took up farming again, to which he added the duties of exciseman, but Burns made no success of either occupation : his muse was all he cared for. His best-known longer poems are *The Cottar's Saturday Night* and *Tam o' Shanter*, the latter having, perhaps, the most popular appeal of all his work.

Byron, George Gordon ; Lord (1788-1824). Son of Captain John Byron and great-nephew of the then Lord Byron, to whose title he succeeded in 1798. His early life was spent at Aberdeen, but he was educated at Harrow and Trinity College, Cambridge. The first of his works to attract attention were his *Hours of Idleness* (1807) and the satirical *English Bards and Scotch Reviewers* (1809). In 1809 he went abroad, and the fruit of two years' travel was the opening cantos of *Childe Harold*, which, published in 1812, made him famous overnight. In 1815 he married Anne Isabella Milbanke, but the union did not prove happy, and Byron went abroad again. His great unfinished work, *Don Juan*, was written in Venice and Ravenna. He never returned to his native land, and in 1823 he offered his services to the Greek insurgents. He died at Missolonghi, where he contracted malarial fever.

Campbell, Thomas (1777-1844). Son of a merchant. Educated at Glasgow University, he afterwards read law at Edinburgh. One of his chief poems, *The Pleasures of Hope*, appeared when he was only twenty-one. His other longer poems include *Gertrude of Wyoming* and *Theodoric*, but his fame rests mainly on his patriotic lyrics, such as *Ye Mariners of England*, *Hohenlinden*, and *The Battle of the Baltic*. Campbell was Lord Rector of Glasgow University for some years, but lived in London during the latter part of his life. His death took place at Boulogne, where he had gone for his health. He is buried in Westminster Abbey.

" Carroll, Lewis " (1833-1898), the *nom de plume* of the Rev. Charles Lutwidge Dodgson. He was born at Daresbury, Cheshire, where his father was Rector. He was educated at Rugby and Oxford, and afterwards took orders. He was appointed Lecturer in mathematics at Oxford, and published several treatises on this subject. His fame, however, rests entirely upon his books for children, which for wit and ingenuity have never been equalled in English literature. His most famous prose works are *Alice's Adventures in Wonderland* and *Through the Looking-Glass*, while *The Hunting of the Snark* and *Phantasmagoria* are regarded as masterpieces of " nonsense " verse.

Chesterton, Gilbert Keith (1874-1936). Born at Campden Hill, Kensington, and educated at St. Paul's School. He studied drawing, mainly with an idea of book illustration, at the Slade School, but eventually gave up art for literature in the form of essays, novels, criticism, and verse. The bulk of his work appeared in the first place in the daily and weekly periodicals of his time. Among his most successful novels may be mentioned *The Napoleon of Notting Hill*, *The Man who was Thursday*, and *The Flying Inn*. His "Father Brown" detective stories show great originality in conception and treatment.

Coleridge, Samuel Taylor (1772-1834).   Born at Ottery St. Mary, Devonshire, where his father was Vicar.   Educated at Christ's Hospital and Jesus College, Cambridge.   He eventually settled at Nether Stowey in Somerset, where he had Wordsworth for a neighbour.   Here Coleridge wrote his most famous poem, *The Rime of the Ancient Mariner*, and also collaborated with his fellow-poet in the *Lyrical Ballads* of 1798.   In 1800 he went to live at Keswick in the Lake District, but soon afterwards his health gave way, chiefly on account of his opium-taking habits. In 1819 he found a home with Dr. Gilman at Highgate, where he died.

Cowper, William (1732-1800).   Born at Great Berkhampstead, Hertfordshire, where his father was Rector.   He was educated at Westminster School, and later studied law at the Middle Temple, being called to the Bar in 1754, though he never practised.   Through family influence he received an appointment as Clerk of the Journals to the House of Lords, but his duties so preyed upon his nervous constitution that his mind gave way for a time.   While unfortunate in many ways Cowper was lucky in his friends, and went to live with the Unwins at Olney in Buckinghamshire, where the Rev. John Newton was curate. Together they produced the famous *Olney Hymns*, of which Cowper wrote sixty-seven.   It was his friend Lady Austin who persuaded him to write his best-known poem in blank verse, *The Task*, and also the lively ballad of *The Diverting History of John Gilpin*, which was based on an actual incident related to him by Lady Austin.   Cowper died at East Dereham in Norfolk.

de la Mare, Walter.   Born in 1873 at Charlton, Kent.   Huguenot by descent, educated at St. Paul's Cathedral Choir School. His work includes poems of fancy, for children, or about them, as in *Songs of Childhood* and *Peacock Pie*, prose romances such as *The Return* and *Memoirs of a Midget*, and distinguished anthologies such as *Come Hither* and *Behold This Dreamer*.

Dobson, Henry Austin (1840-1921). Born at Plymouth and educated at Beaumaris Grammar School and abroad. Entered the Civil Service in 1856 and remained until 1901. He owes his literary reputation to his work on eighteenth-century subjects, in which he showed a profound knowledge and a delicate imagination both in prose and verse. He wrote many biographical studies, in addition to essays on the lighter phases and issues of his particular period. His work in verse in *Proverbs in Porcelain*, *At the Sign of the Lyre*, and other volumes, was of a very graceful and accomplished order. In prose he is famous for his *Eighteenth Century Vignettes*, while perhaps *The Ballad of Beau Brocade* has enjoyed as wide a popularity as anything he wrote.

Doyle, Arthur Conan (1859-1930). Born at Edinburgh, the son of Charles Doyle, an artist, and nephew of the well-known " Dicky " Doyle who drew the famous cover-design of *Punch*. Conan Doyle was educated at Stonyhurst and Edinburgh University. He practised medicine in his early years, but gave this up for literature, in which he met with marked success. He is chiefly known as the creator of " Sherlock Holmes," who first appeared in *A Study in Scarlet* in 1889, which was followed two years later by *The Sign of Four*, though it was the short stories that really made Sherlock Holmes world-famous. Conan Doyle also wrote many historical novels, among which *Micah Clarke* and *The White Company* are the best known. In addition he wrote several outstanding books on military subjects. His chief interest in his later years lay in the study and defence of spiritualism.

Doyle, Sir Francis Hastings (1810-1888). A poet who came from a long line of military ancestors. Born at Tadcaster, Yorkshire, and educated at Eton and Oxford. He studied law, being called to the Bar in 1837, and later was appointed Commissioner of Customs. He was for ten years Professor of Poetry at Oxford. In 1834 he published *Miscellaneous Verse*, followed by many other poems popular in their day, but now mainly forgotten save two ballads that have never lost their popular appeal—*The Private of the Buffs* and *The Loss of the Birkenhead*.

Biographical Notes

Goldsmith, Oliver (1728-1774). Son of an Irish clergyman and born at Pallasmore, Co. Longford, Ireland. His early education was at the village school and local grammar school, but he went at fourteen to Trinity College, Dublin. After leaving he studied medicine, travelled abroad, and reached London penniless in 1756. He occupied himself as a doctor, teacher, actor, and hack writer, often producing brilliant work with very little reward. His literary gifts, however, won him the lifelong friendship of Dr. Johnson and other famous men, who, in spite of his eccentric habits, all loved the good-hearted Irishman. Goldsmith found fame in three different forms of expression : the poem, as in *The Deserted Village* ; the novel, as in *The Vicar of Wakefield* ; and the drama, as in *She Stoops to Conquer*—all of which are of the highest merit. Goldsmith died in London, and is buried in the Temple Church.

Gray, Thomas (1716-1771). Born in London, the son of a scrivener. He was educated at Eton and Cambridge, and after leaving the latter he travelled abroad with his school-friend Horace Walpole. Most of Gray's life was spent at Cambridge, where he was appointed to the Professorship of Modern History. His fame rests almost entirely on a small group of poems, including his *Elegy in a Country Churchyard*, which was written mostly at Stoke Poges, Buckinghamshire, the place usually accepted as the scene of the poem. It is doubtful if any poem in English literature has had greater popularity than this. Gray died at Cambridge, but was buried in the peaceful country churchyard which he had rendered immortal.

Hardy, Thomas (1840-1928). Born in Dorsetshire, he went to the village school and then to a day school in Dorchester. The headmaster was an exceptionally able man, who later opened a more advanced school, which Hardy also attended. In early life he studied architecture, which profession he followed for some years. Between 1871 and 1896 he published the great series of stories usually known as " The Wessex Novels," containing such masterpieces as *Tess of the D'Urbervilles*, *Under the Greenwood Tree*, *The Woodlanders*, *The Return of the Native*, and *Jude the Obscure*. The unintelligent hostility shown by critics of this last book caused Hardy to abandon fiction for his first love, poetry, and during the next thirty years he produced such memorable volumes as *Wessex Poems*, *Time's Laughing-stocks*, *Human Shows* and *Winter Words*, and his wonderful epic-drama, *The Dynasts*. He received the Order of Merit in 1910. His ashes lie in Poets' Corner in Westminster Abbey.

Hawker, Robert Stephen (1804-1875). Born at Stoke Damerel, Devon, and educated at Cheltenham and Oxford, he later became Vicar of Morwenstow, a community on the Cornish coast, with a long tradition of smuggling. Of his Cornish Ballads the most famous is *The Song of the Western Men*, supposed to have been sung by the miners at the time of the trial of the Seven Bishops. Both Scott and Macaulay took it to be a real fragment from an ancient poem.

Henley, William Ernest (1849-1903). Born at Gloucester. His first poems were written while he was a patient in Edinburgh Hospital, where he met Robert Louis Stevenson. He became a very influential figure in London journalism as the editor of *The Magazine of Art*, *The New Review* and *The Scots* (*National*) *Observer*. He collaborated with Stevenson in several dramas. Henley's poems, grouped under such titles as *Echoes*, *Hawthorn and Lavender*, *London Voluntaries*, *For England's Sake*, are perhaps rather uneven in quality, but they show an extraordinary command of rich and resonant language, great skill in such difficult forms as the ballade and rondeau, and simplicity and poignancy in the short lyric.

Herrick, Robert (1591-1674). Born in London and apprenticed to his uncle Sir William Herrick, a goldsmith, for ten years. Later he went to Cambridge and eventually took orders. He was appointed to Dean Prior, a remote parish in Devonshire, from which he was ejected on political grounds, returning at the Restoration of Charles II. His best-known poems are contained in his *Noble Numbers* and *Hesperides*. Such lyrics as *Daffodils*, *Gather ye rosebuds*, *Cherry Ripe*, and a hundred others, are unsurpassed for their grace and tunefulness in English verse of any period.

Hodgson, Ralph, was born in Yorkshire in 1871, and worked for some years in Fleet Street. In 1924 he became lecturer on

English Literature at Sendai University in Japan. Nearly every poem he has written—*The Song of Honour, The Bull, The Bells of Heaven, Time, you old gipsy man, The Gipsy Girl, Eve*—has become famous. Few writers have made so wide a reputation with work that forms so small a volume as his *Poems* (1917).

Hood, Thomas (1799-1845). Son of a London bookseller. Educated at Clapham he entered a merchant's office when he was thirteen. He later went to Dundee, where his first poems were published, and returned to London in 1818. For some time he studied as an engraver, but eventually took to writing as his true vocation. His artistic work, however, is seen in his illustrations in *Hood's Magazine* and other journals. Hood is nowadays remembered for his serious shorter poems, of which *The Song of the Shirt, The Bridge of Sighs, The Haunted House* and *I remember* are the most celebrated examples, though his punning, humorous verses enjoyed a great vogue in their day. Hood's later years were clouded by ill-health and poverty.

Houghton, Lord : Richard Monckton Milnes (1809-1885). Son of Robert Pemberton Milnes, M.P., he was educated privately and at Cambridge. He sat in the House of Commons as member for Pontefract from 1837 till 1863, when he was raised to the peerage. At Cambridge he had become intimate with Tennyson, Hallam and Thackeray, and he remained all his life the patron and friend of artists and men of letters. His own graceful and reflective work was much admired in its day and still retains its charm.

Hunt, James Henry Leigh (1784-1859). Born at Southgate, Middlesex, and educated at Christ's Hospital. With his brother he started a weekly paper, *The Examiner*, but an alleged libel on the Prince Regent led to Hunt's imprisonment for two years. During his imprisonment he was visited by several famous literary men and wrote his narrative poem *The Story of Rimini*. His *Poetical Works* appeared in 1819. He later joined Lord Byron in Italy and with him started another journal, which again did not succeed chiefly owing to quarrels between the two editors. Subsequently Hunt started still another paper, *The London Journal*, which was more successful.

His unbusinesslike ways kept him in difficulties all his life. Leigh Hunt's poems have descriptive power and brightness, but his chief literary fame now rests on his essays, which are full of charm. His best-known prose works are *The Old Court Suburb*, the story of Old Kensington, *The Town*, a description of Old London, and *Men, Women, and Books*.

Jonson, Ben (1573-1637). Born in London and educated at Westminster School. After being apprenticed to his stepfather, a master bricklayer, he joined the Army and served in the Netherlands, but later became an actor and playwright. In the latter capacity many successful dramas came from his pen, among which are *Volpone*, *The Alchemist*, *Sejanus*, *Epicene* or *The Silent Woman*, and *Every Man in his Humour*. Jonson was the founder of a new style of English comedy and had a powerful influence on his contemporaries. He himself refers to his friendship with Shakespeare and their meetings at the Mermaid Tavern, in Eastcheap, and his masques and court entertainments made him perhaps the most successful of Jacobean dramatists.

Keats, John (1795-1821). Son of a livery-stable keeper, Keats was educated at a school at Enfield, Middlesex, and later apprenticed to a doctor at Edmonton. He soon gave up medicine, however, for literature. His first book of poems appeared in 1817, but was not at all successful. In 1818 his narrative poem *Endymion* incurred a savage attack in *Blackwood's Magazine* and the *Quarterly Review*; but his 1820 volume contained a series of masterpieces—*The Eve of St. Agnes*, *Hyperion*, *Isabella*, and the odes *To Autumn*, *To a Nightingale*, and *On a Grecian Urn*. By this time consumption had declared itself, and Keats set out for Italy in search of health in September, 1820. In the following February he died at Rome, where his tombstone bears his own epitaph : " Here lies one whose name was writ in water."

Kingsley, Charles (1819-1875). Son of a clergyman, he was born at Holne, near Dartmoor in Devonshire. He was educated at King's College, London, and Cambridge. In 1842 he was ordained, and became Rector of Eversley in Hampshire, where he spent the greater part of his life. He was an extremely versatile writer, deeply interested in the social and scientific problems of his day, as well as in historical, classical and religious themes. His greatest novels—*Westward Ho!*, *Hypatia* and *Hereward the Wake*—are all different in setting, and his most successful books for children were *The Water Babies* and the Greek myths retold in *The Heroes*. His poems include such favourites as the *Ode to the North East Wind*, *The Three Fishers* and *A Farewell*.

Kipling, Rudyard (1865-1936). Born in Bombay, India, the son of J. Lockwood Kipling. He was educated at the United Services College, Westward Ho, Devonshire. He began his literary career in journalism in India, and also travelled extensively before settling in England. His reputation was first made by his stories and verses on the life of soldiers, officials and natives in India, in such volumes as *Plain Tales*, *Soldiers Three*, *Life's Handicap*, *Departmental Ditties* and *Barrack-Room Ballads*. Younger readers were captivated by his two *Jungle Books*, his *Just So Stories*, and the tales based on English history in *Puck of Pook's Hill* and *Rewards and Fairies*. His later years were also very productive, and no one wrote with more power and effect on the great national and imperial issues of his time.

Longfellow, Henry Wadsworth (1807-1882). Born at Portland, Maine, U.S.A., the son of a lawyer. He was educated at Bowdoin College, where he later became Professor of Modern Languages, a post he held subsequently also at Harvard University. Later he travelled extensively in Europe and England. His most important works are *Hiawatha*, *The Golden Legend*, *Evangeline* and *The Courtship of Miles Standish* ; but such shorter poems as *The Wreck of the Hesperus*, *Excelsior*, *The Village Blacksmith*, *A Psalm of Life*, *The Children's Hour*, *The Belfry of Bruges*, and others too numerous to mention, show no signs of losing their popularity. Longfellow was a man of noble and chivalrous character, much loved by all his contemporaries alike in England and his native country.

Macaulay, Thomas Babington ; Lord (1800-1859). Son of Zachary Macaulay, a Scottish philanthropist and opponent of

slavery. Born at Rothly Temple, Leicestershire, he was educated at a private school at Clapham and Trinity College,
Cambridge. He studied law and entered Parliament, and in
1834 was appointed legal adviser to the Supreme Council of
India. His Memorandum, which decided the westernisation
of Indian education, was a landmark in imperial history. On
his return after four years he became Secretary for War and
Paymaster to the Forces. In 1842 he published the *Lays of
Ancient Rome* and in 1843 his collected *Essays*, which had an
amazing welcome. His *History of England*, though never com-
pleted, at once took rank as a classic.

Marvell, Andrew (1621-1678). Son of the Rector of Winestead,
Yorkshire, where he was born. He was educated at Hull and
Cambridge, and later spent some years abroad. His early
literary career was mainly as a political writer, but his fame
rests entirely upon his poetical works and such delightful lyrics
as *Thoughts in a Garden*, *The Nymph regretting the loss of her Fawn*,
The Bermudas, and the noble *Horatian Ode upon Cromwell's Return*.
At one time Marvell sat as M.P. for Hull, and was for some
years Latin Secretary to John Milton. Marvell lived on Highgate Hill for the last years of his life.

Masefield, John (born 1874). Famous alike as poet and novelist,
he was created Poet Laureate in 1930. Among his poetical
works the following are perhaps the most celebrated : *The
Everlasting Mercy*, *The Widow in the Bye Street*, *The Daffodil Fields*,
Salt Water Ballads and *Reynard the Fox*. His plays include *The
Tragedy of Nan*, *Philip the King* and *Good Friday*. In prose his chief
works are *Captain Margaret*, *Sard Harker*, *Odtaa* and *Dead Nick*.

Milton, John (1608-1674). Son of a scrivener, he was born in
Bread Street, London, and educated at St. Paul's School and
Christ's College, Cambridge. He afterwards lived at Horton,
near Windsor, where he wrote *L'Allegro*, *Il Penseroso* and *Lycidas*,
and the masques of *Arcades* and *Comus*. In 1638 he studied
abroad and on his return settled in London, where he produced
a series of powerful political pamphlets, among them his noble
Areopagitica. In 1649 he was appointed Latin Secretary to the
Council of State. His epic *Paradise Lost* was published in 1667,

and was partly written at Chalfont St. Giles, where he had retired during the Great Plague of London. This was followed in 1671 by *Paradise Regained* and *Samson Agonistes*. Milton, who was totally blind for many years, was three times married.

Neale, John Mason (1818-1866). Born in London, the son of the Rev. Cornelius Neale. Educated at Blackheath, Farnham and Sherborne, and at Trinity College, Cambridge. Neale spent most of his early life and many of his later years at Shepperton, Middlesex, which appears in his historical novel *Shepperton Manor* (1844). It is, however, as a hymn-writer that he is best remembered, and among his works are such favourites as "Jerusalem the Golden," "Art thou weary, art thou languid" and "Brief life is here our portion."

Newbolt, Sir Henry John (1862-1938). Born at Bilston, Staffordshire, and educated at Clifton College and Corpus Christi College, Oxford. He practised as a barrister until 1897. His literary reputation was made in 1897 by his *Admirals All*, and he continued to be chiefly famous for his patriotic verse and ballads of the sea. He was knighted in 1915 and became a Companion of Honour in 1922. He also wrote several books on military subjects, in addition to a *Naval History of the Great War*.

Noyes, Alfred. Born in 1880 in Staffordshire and educated at Exeter College, Oxford. His first volume of poems, *The Loom of Years*, appeared in 1902, and was followed by *Drake*, a grand Elizabethan epic, 1906-08 ; *Forty Singing Seamen* in 1907 ; *The Enchanted Island*, and other volumes of verse and prose, leading up to an epic of scientific discovery entitled *The Torchbearers*. His *Flower of Old Japan* and many shorter poems were set to music by distinguished composers. From 1914 to 1923 he was Professor of English Literature at Princeton University, U.S.A.

Patmore, Coventry Kersey Dighton (1823-1896). Born at Woodford, Essex, and spent most of his life in the Printed Book department of the British Museum. His verses are full of graceful thought, but are now little read. His poetical masterpiece was his work *The Angel in the House*, a celebration of married love.

Peacock, Thomas Love (1785-1866). Born at Weymouth, Dorset, son of a London merchant, he attended various schools, but was mainly self-educated, though he became a learned scholar. He was for many years in the India Office, where he rose to be Chief Examiner. He was a close friend of Shelley and father-in-law of George Meredith. His novels, *Gryll Grange*, *Crotchet Castle*, *Headlong Hall*, *Nightmare Abbey*, *Maid Marian*, have been described as " whimsical and unique, full of paradox and prejudice and a curious learning, with witty dialogue and occasional poems interspersed." Peacock lived for many years at Halliford Green, Middlesex, where he died.

Procter, Adelaide Ann (1825-1864). Eldest daughter of Bryan Waller Procter (" Barry Cornwall "). Many of her poems were published in *Household Words* and *All the Year Round*. She took great interest in social questions affecting women. She wrote many songs and hymns, but by far the most famous of all her writings were the words to Sullivan's song, *The Lost Chord*.

Scott, Sir Walter (1771-1832). Son of a Writer to the Signet and born in Edinburgh. He was educated at the High School and University there, where he studied law. In 1806 he became Clerk to the Court of Sessions, but his heart was in literature, and in 1802 he had already published his *Minstrelsy of the Scottish Border*, followed in 1805 by *The Lay of the Last Minstrel*. In 1814 he published *Waverley*, the first of his superb historical novels (including *Ivanhoe*, *The Talisman*, *Kenilworth*), which established his fame, though it was not till 1827 that he acknowledged their authorship. He became a baronet in 1819. The bankruptcy of the printing and bookselling businesses with which he was connected caused him to shorten his life by heroic efforts to work off the debts, and he died at his famous house, Abbotsford, on the Tweed.

Shakespeare, William (1564-1616). The greatest poet and dramatist in all English literature was born at Stratford-on-Avon, Warwickshire, and educated at the Grammar School of that town. At the age of eighteen he married Ann Hathaway, of Shottery. A few years later he made his way to London, where he became an actor, and later a writer of plays. It is impossible here to mention all his plays, but they fall into three divisions, the histories, the comedies, and the tragedies. They enjoyed enormous popularity, and by 1611 he had become a rich man, and was able to return to Stratford and purchase local property, including a large house, New Place, where he spent his last years. His tomb in Stratford Church is a place of pilgrimage for people from all over the world.

Shelley, Percy Bysshe (1792-1822). Son of Sir Timothy Shelley, was born at Field Place, Horsham, Sussex, and educated at Syon Academy, Brentford, Middlesex, Eton, and University College, Oxford, whence he was expelled for writing on atheism. In the same year, 1811, he married Harriet Westbrook. His first notable work in verse was *Queen Mab*, written in 1813. In 1814 he eloped to Switzerland with Mary, daughter of William Godwin, but soon returned to England and wrote his *Alastor*. In 1816 he went to Geneva and became a close friend of Byron. The suicide of his first wife in that year led to his marriage with Mary Godwin, and in 1817 appeared another great poem, *The Revolt of Islam*. In 1818 he left England once more, as it proved for ever. He went to Italy, where he produced *Prometheus Unbound* and other magnificent poems and dramas. He was drowned in a boating accident, and his ashes were buried in Rome, near the grave of Keats.

Southey, Robert (1774-1843). Son of a linen-draper and born at Bristol. He was educated at Westminster School and Oxford. After a period of foreign travel he settled at Greta Hall, Keswick. Here he spent many years in literary work and formed with Coleridge and Wordsworth the influential Lake School of Poets. He was an amazingly prolific writer in almost every vein, but his great epics are nowadays unread, and he is remembered for one or two short poems, *The Inchcape Rock*, *The Battle of Blenheim*, *My Days among the Dead are past*, and his admirable *Lives* of Nelson and Wesley. He was Poet Laureate from 1813 until his death, which occurred at Keswick.

Spring Rice, Sir Cecil Arthur (1859-1918). Educated at Eton and Balliol College, Oxford, where he was conspicuous as a classical scholar. He held several diplomatic posts, notably as

British Ambassador to U.S.A. during the Great War of 1914-1918.

Squire, Sir John Collings. Born at Plymouth in 1884 and educated at Blundell's School, Tiverton, and St. John's College, Cambridge. He became editor of the *New Statesman* and founded the *London Mercury*. His serious poems include *The Three Hills*, *The Moon*, *A Face in Candlelight*, and many other volumes, and his brilliant parodies appear in *Steps to Parnassus* and *Tricks of the Trade*. His criticisms are collected in *Books in General*, *Essays at Large*, *Sunday Mornings*, etc., and short stories in *Grub Street Nights' Entertainments* and *Outside Eden*. He also collaborated in a highly successful play, *Berkeley Square*.

Stevenson, Robert Louis (1850-1894). Born at Edinburgh, the son of a civil engineer. He was always of delicate constitution, and though he was called to the Bar he never practised. A canoe tour led to his first real book, *An Inland Voyage*, in 1878, and the next year a land tour produced his *Travels with a Donkey*. It was the publication of *Treasure Island* some years later, however, that made him world-famous, and this was followed by a striking series of romances in *Kidnapped*, *Catriona*, *The Black Arrow* and *The Master of Ballantrae*. Some of his macabre short stories, such as *Dr. Jekyll and Mr. Hyde*, show his genius in quite a different light. Stevenson eventually settled in Samoa for reasons of health and died there.

Tennyson, Alfred ; Lord (1809-1892). Son of the Rector of Somersby, Lincolnshire, and educated at Louth Grammar School and Trinity College, Cambridge. From the *Poems, chiefly Lyrical*, of 1830, the *Poems* of 1833, the two volumes of 1842, *The Princess* in 1847, *In Memoriam* in 1850, *Maud* in 1855, and the *Idylls of the King* in 1859 to *The Death of Oenone* in 1892, he produced a series of masterpieces which gained him a position rarely attained by any writer in his own lifetime, and won him the Poet Laureateship in 1850 and a peerage in 1884. Tennyson died at his house, " Aldworth," near Haslemere, and was buried in Westminster Abbey.

Thomson, James (1700-1748). Born at Ednam, Roxburghshire, and educated at Jedburgh and Edinburgh. He was intended for the Church, but gave up this idea and went to London in 1725. His first poem was *Winter*, which was followed by *Summer*, *Spring* and *Autumn* ; the four being finally published together under the general title of *The Seasons*. For some years he travelled abroad as tutor to the Solicitor-General's son. Eventually his friends and patrons obtained him a government sinecure. *The Castle of Indolence*, possibly his best work, appeared in 1748. As a dramatist Thomson was not successful, though his *Masque of Alfred* is remembered as introducing *Rule, Britannia*. His literary life was spent in Richmond, Surrey, where he is buried.

Whittier, John Greenleaf (1807-1892). Born at Boston, Mass., U.S.A., and often known as " The Quaker Poet " on account of his ancestry. In early life he worked on a farm, but finally entered literature through politics, being an ardent adherent to the cause of Anti-Slavery. By his writings, both as a poet and a journalist, he did much to stimulate national feeling in the cause of freedom. Isolated pieces such as *The Pipes of Lucknow*, *Snow-Bound*, *Maud Muller* and *Barbara Frietchie* keep his memory green when more ambitious work has been forgotten.

Wolfe, Charles (1791-1823). Born in Dublin and educated at Winchester and Trinity College, Dublin. He took orders and became Rector of Donoughmore, but his health failed and he died of consumption at an early age. His fame as a poet rests entirely upon the universally admired *Burial of Sir John Moore*, which first appeared anonymously in an Irish newspaper.

Wordsworth, William (1770-1850). Son of a land-agent, he was born at Cockermouth. He was educated at Penrith and Hawkshead and St. John's College, Cambridge, and was greatly influenced by his experience in France when the revolutionary movement was at its height. In collaboration with Coleridge he produced in 1798 the volume of *Lyrical Ballads* which influenced so profoundly the course of English literature. As the leader of the Lake School he established a reputation which grew with the changing taste in poetic methods and ideals, and in 1843 he succeeded his friend Southey as Poet Laureate. He was buried in the little churchyard at Grasmere, close to his old home.

Made and Printed in
Great Britain by C. Tinling & Co. Limited
Liverpool, London and Prescot